IRISH TALES OF TERROR

IRISH
Tales of Terror

Edited by Jim McGarry

Collins
FONTANA BOOKS

First published by Fontana Books 1971
Second Impression May 1976

The arrangement of this collection is copyright
© J. N. McGarry 1970

Made and printed in Great Britain by
William Collins Sons & Co Ltd Glasgow

CONTENTS

ACKNOWLEDGEMENTS

The Editor gratefully acknowledges permission to reprint copyright material to the following:

James Reynolds and Farrar, Straus and Giroux Inc. for *The Weeping Wall* and *The Headless Rider of Castle Sheela* from 'Ghosts in Irish Houses' by James Reynolds.

Macmillan and Co. for *The Raid* from 'Innisfallen Fare Thee Well' by Sean O'Casey.

Shane Leslie and Hutchinson and Co., Ltd. for *The Diplomatist's Story* by Shane Leslie.

M. B. Yeats and Macmillan and Co. for *The Sorcerers* by W. B. Yeats from his collection 'Mythologies' published by Macmillan and Co.

The Clonmel Witch Burning and *The Island Magee Terror* are copyright © J. N. McGarry 1971.

The folk-lore items between the stories are by Esperanza, Lady Wilde.

EDITOR'S NOTE

INTRODUCTION

Beneath the lighthearted and carefree image which he so often wears, the Irishman has a deep core of superstition and fear of the unknown, going back through the centuries.

Terror in Irish literature mainly involves ghostly tales—not because authors have necessarily wanted to confine themselves to the medium of ghost stories, but rather stemming from the traditional superstitions which for hundreds of years dominated the folklore of the people. I have tried in this anthology to put together a varied collection of stories, many of which do not rely on the theme of hauntings which are, after all, only one manifestation of terror. Some afford an insight into an Ireland and a way of life now vanished, while others show characteristics common to terror the world over.

The settings of the stories and their events are not localised in any one part of the island but embrace Ireland and its people: North, South, East and West. From rocky, windswept Island Magee on the far North East coast the reader is carried to a dim, dark Dublin tenement. An ancestral house overlooking bleakly beautiful Lough Allen in the Leitrim mountains is in sharp contrast to the humble cottage in the fertile hills of Tipperary.

The names of Sean O'Casey and W. B. Yeats, two of the most distinguished Irish writers of this century, need no introduction to the reader. Sean O'Casey's extract *The Raid* is set in the period of the Anglo-Irish war, around 1920. It expresses poignantly the terror of an Irish soldier in hiding during a house-to-house search by the Black and Tans. His thoughts and anxieties are vividly described, as from his hiding place he hears the movements of his enemy only a few feet away. Yeats on the other hand talks of a session he underwent with a group of sorcerers. He describes the atmosphere in which he had to struggle against falling into the mysterious trance that had laid hold of his companions. Whilst they invoked various spirits and addressed unseen forces he fought

9

to prevent himself from entering the same sinister oblivion. The experience of the powers of darkness remained horribly imprinted on his mind for a long time after.

Carleton's *Wildgoose Lodge* describes how a peaceful community was drawn by a few leaders into a terrifying plot for the destruction of a household. It is a timeless example of how a mass can be led almost unwittingly to participate in deeds of horror. *Melmoth* is an extraordinary account of a most sinister death scene, re-created brilliantly by Charles Maturin's detailed description of character and atmosphere. Ghost stories being inevitable to any book of Irish terror, I have endeavoured to choose five such stories as dissimilar in their content as possible. *The Dream* I consider to be among the best tales of Joseph Sheridan Le Fanu, the acknowledged master of terror. And in modern times, James Reynolds and Shane Leslie have universal recognition for the quality of their Irish Ghost Stories. Reynolds' *Weeping Wall* is a most readable story with an added interest that it links Ireland with Poland in an uncanny set of events. Normally, in an anthology such as this, one would not consider including two stories by the same author. However, his *Headless Rider of Castle Sheela* is of such a quality as to also demand its inclusion. *The Diplomatist's Story* tells of the strange influence on a man's life of an apparition seen during a night spent in an Irish castle, and Patrick Bardan's *The Warning* combines romance and the ghostly in a fashion at once charming and frightening.

The practice of witchcraft has never been as widespread in Ireland as it has been on the Continent of Europe. I first became acquainted with the *Island Magee Terror* from very old sources and was immediately struck by its incredible resemblance to the story of the Witches of Salem, in New England. That the Irish events took place a short twenty years after those in America and that sea captains from the Island Magee area were in constant communication across the Atlantic greatly heightened my interest. Two other features of this story were particularly impressive. The simple community of North East Ireland, when faced with witchcraft and all its consequences, showed an immense zeal for justice during the investigation and trial. However, the sentences imposed on the miscreants were hallmarked by a leniency which it would have been almost impossible to find elsewhere at a time when witches were being burned on slender or non-existent evidence.

No account of the World of Terror in this book seems to me to compare for its sheer horror with the *Clonmel Witch Burning*. It is unique in that it took place as late as the year 1895 and was therefore quite probably the last witch burning in Europe. The story entwines elements of sadism, extreme cruelty, callous indifference to human life, and the dreadful consequences of superstitious ignorance. It is a factual account of an event that stands out in the chronicles of its time.

The folklore extracts between the stories are by Speranza, Lady Wilde, mother of Oscar Wilde, and were collected by her from traditional sources. They illustrate the folk legends of the people—legends which were so often behind the creation of the stories in this book.

In conclusion I would like to offer my special thanks to my daughter Mary who, unsparing of time and hard work, enabled me by her assistance to compile this book.

JIM MCGARRY

IRISH SUPERSTITIONS

Whitsuntide is a most unlucky time; horses foaled then will grow up to be dangerous killers.
A child born at Whitsuntide will have an evil temper, and may commit a murder.
Water is dangerous at Whitsuntide, for an evil power is on the waves and the lakes and the rivers, and a boat may be swamped and men drowned unless a bride steers; then the danger ceases.

When a seventh son is born, if an earth-worm is put into the infant's hand and kept there till it dies, the child will have power to charm away all diseases.

When a family has been carried off by fever, the house where they died may be again inhabited with safety if a certain number of sheep are driven in to sleep there for three nights.

It is unlucky to accept a lock of hair or a four-footed beast from a lover.

The seventh son of a seventh son has power over all diseases, and can cure them by laying on of hands; and a son born after his father's death has power over fevers.

THE WEEPING WALL

JAMES REYNOLDS

Sometimes it happens that ghostly visitations run in parallels. At a given time of day or night, either simultaneously or a few minutes apart, the identical manifestations will appear in two or more houses, many miles apart, even in different countries. This is true in the case of the occurrences at Castle Sczriny in Poland and Drumshambo in County Leitrim in Ireland.

That part of the story began in 1873, when a young Irish woman named Considine of Drumshambo, a late Georgian house standing in a run-down waste of parkland on the Lough Allen near Ballyfarnon, married a young cavalry officer whom she met at the Dublin Horse Show.

The young man, a younger son of the Polish family of Sczriny, fell madly in love with the handsome Irish horsewoman, paid ardent court to her, and, a few weeks after their meeting, the two were married at ancient Castle Bran, near Dunkineely in Donegal, the house of Miss Considine's grandmother. Thus were the Hispano-Irish House of Considine and the Polish House of Sczriny united.

Count Alexander Sczriny took his bride to Paris on their honeymoon. While in Paris the new Countess met various members of the Guise family, related to the Sczriny by marriage. In Italy she met members of the powerful Gonzaga. Here again there were family connections, for in 1660, Louise Marie, daughter of Ruggiero Gonzaga, Tyrant of Mantua, had married the King of Poland. In turn her daughter had married a Sczriny. So by the reading of marriage vows, and ring slipped on her finger, the rather hoydenish, grey-eyed daughter of an unimportant Irish squireen from a remote house in the back country of County Leitrim found herself related by marriage to a number of the most important families in Europe.

The erstwhile Miss Considine was to learn that these families

14

had long histories of dark doings. Treachery and murder were rampant on the Gonzaga rolls. Greed for power and over-weening arrogance which made many enemies were on the side of the Sczriny.

The Sczriny grandson of the Gonzaga queen of Poland came into the family fortunes at sixteen. His grandmother signified she wished him named Stephan. A volatile, handsome boy, he showed early signs of mental instability.

Count Stephan Sczriny repudiated the authority of his mother and guardian, his father's uncle, Prince Oransky. He listened to no one and rode roughshod over nobles and peasantry alike. He squandered such vast sums of money on debaucheries of every kind that at last a family conclave convened. Somehow Stephan must be restrained, else the Sczriny fortune would soon melt away. Hoping he would listen to reason, his uncle invited Count Stephan to the Oransky Castle near Crakow, where he planned to entertain a hunting party and gradually to show his nephew that living off the rich lands of the Sczriny-Oransky estates had immense attraction and security. But whatever hopes he harboured were destined to failure even before Stephan arrived. For he arrived in a drunken, surly mood, and if one watched him closely, stark fear lay at the back of his eyes.

In this year of 1714, it was the custom in Poland for a noble to carry a whip at all times, as a sign of power more than anything else, though in the hands of such as Count Stephan Sczriny the whip often drew a pattern of welts across the back or cheek of a serf slow to do his bidding. The night of his arrival at the castle he became so violent that Prince Oransky realized he could bear with him no longer. As the night waxed late, Stephan became so fuddled with excessive drinking that he lay back in his chair in a coma. It was then his uncle had servants half drag the drooling figure of his young nephew to an iron-barred room high in a tower of the castle.

For days Stephan railed against his imprisonment to no avail; then, in a burst of rage and bravado, he told his uncle why he had indulged in this last debauch: fear—fear it was. He had raped a young village girl near Vornov, the village

15

nearest to Castle Sczriny. He feared he had killed her. If she died, he feared for his life at the hands of the townspeople. He begged his uncle to go to Vornov and find out how matters stood. Prince Oransky recoiled in horror at this tale. He felt the power of his family would be able to weather almost any escapade indulged in by his irresponsible nephew, but murder of a young girl placed Stephan beyond the pale and within the grasp of the King's provost.

Before any action whatever could be taken by Prince Oransky, word was brought to him that a delegation of men from Vornov were in the outer court, demanding that he receive them. The proud but wretched man stepped quietly out on a balcony overlooking the court. He listened to a man who stood out from the group of fifteen or twenty villagers standing in the bright sunlight.

The spokesman, a tall old man, the patriarch of the village of Vornov, told his story simply and with eloquence. It was a dreadful story—a young girl of fifteen, pursued by Count Stephan, ridden down and trampled under the hoofs of his horse, then raped as she lay dying. The people of Vornov demanded he hand over his nephew for trial.

Prince Oransky bowed his consent. He had not uttered a word, though every word of the tall old man had burned into his brain.

Later that day a strange, grim party of men set out for Vornov. A few of the village men rode ahead of the prisoner, the remainder, behind him. Prince Oransky rode beside his nephew in stony silence.

As they came out of the shadowed forest, three of the men rode ahead to meet a number of villagers who came towards them. It was then Count Stephan made his bid for freedom. Being an excellent horseman and well mounted, he cast for freedom, on one chance in ten thousand. Digging spurs into the horse's flanks, he streaked across the field in front of the gates of Vornov, but he did not count on the sure aim of a young boy standing a little apart, the brother of the murdered girl, who stooped, then straightened, with a jagged rock in his hand. Like an arrow from the bow, it curved and struck

Count Stephan just below his right ear. His horse reared, threw him, and galloped off into the woods.

Next morning the village mob was swelled by recruits from outlying villages. Many were the outrages laid at the door of unfortunate Stephan Sczriny. The court-house where he cowered, was stormed, and the terrified youth bound with ropes, was dragged across the square. Mob rule is swift and terrible in its decisions. It is an army with banners. Count Stephan, repudiated by his family, was strung up to a cross-bar erected for the purpose near the village inn.

A cart bearing Stephan's weight was just about to be drawn out from under him when a distraught woman stumbled out from the crowd—the mother of the girl who had been killed. Pointing her finger at the prisoner, she shrieked, 'Never will the Sczriny find peace. Misfortune will follow every bearer of the name, but, because your mother was always kind to me, I will say this: before disaster strikes, the Sczriny will be warned. Yes, they will be warned; if they can stave off impending fate, let them in their arrogance try. Let them try. They will be warned.'

The woman was led away. The rope tightened around the neck of Count Stephan Sczriny, who had brought ruin on his House.

The Wall that Weeps appeared at Castle Sczriny more than a century before the phenomenon was seen in the library at Drumshambo. The first time was one June evening. The moon had risen and the sky was littered with stars.

A servant, bringing food on a tray to a member of the Sczriny family who lay ill in an upstairs room, felt a strange dampness rise from the floor of a small salon through which he was passing. Looking up at the walls, he was amazed and terrified to see streaks of water, like great tears, coursing down one wall from cornice to chair rail. The wall was distempered a dull green, and the dampness had already stained it in long points which made a design very like icicles hanging from a roof in winter.

Hastily placing the tray of food on a side table, the servant ran through the rooms seeking some member of the family.

In the library he found Prince Paul Oransky, son of the Oransky who had delivered Stephan Sczriny to the mob at Vornov a decade before. Prince Paul followed the man servant cautiously, not knowing, from his chattering description of what was happening, just what he would find.

Dark runnels of moisture coursed down the wall—not the four walls, but only the wall opposite him. On this wall hung a large painting of a wolf hunt. Already the canvas seemed waterlogged and bulging.

Then the most curious thing of all happened—the strange manifestation which is seen only by members of the Sczriny-Oransky families at Castle Sczriny, or the Considine family at Drumshambo, never by anyone not a member of these two families who may chance to be in the room at the time the wall weeps. A slow tracing appeared on the wall as if a huge, invisible finger were writing a name, the name of some member of the family. As Prince Paul gazed transfixed, the unseen finger slowly wrote L-A-U-R-I-N. For a second only the name Laurin seemed to blaze upon the wet green wall. Then, as intimation of disaster to one of his family raced through Prince Paul's mind, the name dimmed and faded altogether. The sagging canvas of the wolf hunt tightened. All became as before, a plain green wall on which hung a gold-framed painting in oils.

Quickly he must find Laurin, for he knew that the heir to the Sczriny estates was not at home. Concealing his anxiety, Prince Paul sought out Laurin's mother in the music-room. From Countess Sczriny he learned that his nephew was in Warsaw, but that he was returning that evening. A coach had been sent to meet him at the house of friends about fifteen miles to the north. He had broken the tiresome journey from Warsaw by stopping to dine at Castle Bielany. The Feast of the Pentecost, a three-day festival held each year at Bielany, was in full swing. Many guests came and went at the castle. Laurin Sczriny would lay a wreath of myrtle and place a wax taper at the foot of the 'Shrine for Travellers.'

Even now, past eleven o'clock, he must be on his way to Sczriny.

No coach appeared that night. During the forenoon of the following day, word was brought to Sczriny that Count Laurin had been in an accident. Returning by the forest road, the horses of his coach had become frightened when suddenly sprung upon by hungry wolves, who searched continuously for food in the dry summer woods. The runaway horses had flung the coach against a tree, overturning it. In the wreckage Count Laurin had been found badly crushed. The coachman was dead and the young count was too badly hurt to move from the forester's cottage to which he had been taken.

Later in the day the heir to Sczriny died—so was fulfilled the curse of the mother of Count Stephan Sczriny's victim.

Within twelve years, the curse struck again. It was a hazy evening in late September when the little son of Count Laurin who had been killed in the runaway coach) was returning through the park at Castle Sczriny with his nurse. Small Stephan was eight years old, and was to celebrate his birthday in a few days.

Passing the gates to the paddock enclosure, the nurse was alarmed to see the gates open, for she remembered hearing at lunch that a new stallion bought at Portosk was kept in the paddock awaiting transfer to the farm, three miles away. She called to the boy to hurry, and they were just passing the open gate when, in a cloud of dust, slaver streaming from his mouth, the great red stallion galloped straight for the terrified woman and child. As he came to the spot where they crouched, he rose on his hind legs, pawed the air in rage and sprang upon the cringing woman who sheltered the little boy in her arms.

No one was about. The cries of the nurse went unheard as the wildly plunging horse savaged them both until they lay dead in pools of blood, torn beyond recognition by the powerful iron-shod hoofs. Snorting in the exaltation a maddened animal finds in the kill, the blood-flecked stallion raced across the park and away over the brow of the hill.

When a stable boy found the horrible remains of the nurse and the little Count Stephan, the sun was sinking beyond the

19

hill over which the killer stallion had disappeared. Night came quickly over the tragic house. This was the story told by the mother of the dead boy:

She had gone to her bedroom after lunch to rest for a while. Then, as it neared teatime, she had ordered the special cakes that were so greatly enjoyed by her small son. Later, as, Stephan and his nurse did not return, she had taken tea alone in a sitting-room across the hall from the Green Salon, which, because of its sinister memories, was seldom used unless many guests were in the house. As she sat there, drinking her tea and looking down a ride of trees in the park, hoping to catch a glimpse of her child, she had felt a cold, damp wind play about her feet. A door must be open somewhere. But the day being warm, and it not yet late, how could the current of air be so tomb-like? An open door leading to the great wine cellars under the castle, perhaps. The countess had risen to investigate, when her eye was drawn to the room opposite where she had been sitting. There, in the Green Salon, the wall wept. Her knees seemed unable to support her weight. Cries froze in her throat. She seemed paralyzed, for all within Castle Sczriny knew what this lacy pattern of water descending the dull green walls presaged.

The countess tried to close her eyes so not to see the name that must inevitably appear. But she could not. Some power held her staring at the dripping wall. There—there it was. Slowly, letters so large they covered half of the wall appeared: S-T-E-P-H-A-N. For a moment only, the word stood out clear and bold. Then down came the tears, obliterating the name of her little son. The countess wept, miserably, as she staggered through the hall towards the outer door.

It seemed ages before the distracted woman found anyone, for it was the harvest, and all except the house servants were in the fields. Finally, calling down an areaway, she drew the attention of a footman who came to her. More men were found and hastily dispatched to find Count Stephan and his nurse. It would almost have been better if they had never been found.

Many years later Moira Considine married Count Sczriny and went to Poland to live. The 'Irish Countess', as she came to be called, fitted into life at Castle Sczriny with ease, as one fits a well-made glove to the hand. There has always been a similarity between the Poles and the Irish—their love of horses, freedom, and living in the country and their enjoyment of the sports and rich fruits of the land.

Two children were born to Moira and Alexander Sczriny, a boy and a girl. On the widely spreading estates of Sczriny-Oransky, the children grew up to be healthy, handsome complements to their parents' happy marriage.

The year that young Peter was fourteen and his sister Maria was ten, they accompanied their father and mother to Ireland to visit the Considine grandmother at Drumshambo. Neither of them had been to Ireland since they were babies and were eager to see their mother's rambling old house on the Lough Allen. She had told them much of the happy childhood that had been hers, running wild with the ponies and later with the big horses, and sailing a small red curragh of her own on the sparkling Lough.

She had rigged up a sail once, when her own could not be found in the boathouse. She had taken a white satin evening wrap belonging to Lady Barrymore, who was staying at Drumshambo. How beautiful it had looked, belling out in the stiff breeze. She had set her dolls in the stern and told them this was a royal barge and that only a Considine could manage satin sails. And then, that evening, the terrible hue and cry, the tat-a ra-ra that had resulted, when the missing wrap was produced from the boathouse, sadly the worse for wear. Old Lady Barrymore had been very decent about it, but her father had whaled Moira properly. Her behind had been a very tender area for days.

Then, there were tales of hunting with the Tipperary and the Clonmel hounds, and the wonderful hunt balls, and the Dublin Horse Show, where she had had the grand fortune to meet their father.

Everyone and everything at Drumshambo looked exactly as they had pictured it, even to old Terry Bannery, the autocrat of the stable yard. He had ruled the roost at Drumshambo, lo, these many years and had taught their mother to ride like a streak of lightning across the trappiest country and to take the great stone and sod banks in flying style. Terry was at the station in Ballyallen to greet them. This summer promised to be pure heaven for the two children.

The weeks sped on. Summer had proved even more satisfying than Peter and Maria Sczriny had hoped, if that was possible. In ten days now they must return to Poland. The count and countess were going to Paris with their grandmother a few days before: then their grandfather would take them to Paris later, where they would join their parents. The family would then return to Poland together.

Three days before the count and his wife were leaving for the Continent, it began to storm. A high wind whipped across the Lough, gaining in force as the second day set in, wild and wet.

The old house creaked and rumbled on its foundations and in every timber under the tiles. Grandfather Considine said that in a storm it always seemed to him more like being in an old hulk rounding the Horn than safe on land inside Drumshambo. 'This old Ark,' he called it.

For years repairs had been necessary at Drumshambo. The roof was noticeably unsafe. Squirrels had gnawed gaps in the timber eaves that supported the heavy roof of the old Charles II wing. But life at Drumshambo followed the line of least resistance. One day, all needed repairs would be attended to. For the present, a new boat was needed on the Lough. Stone walls along the South meadows must be repaired to keep the Kerry cattle from straying. Let the roof leak for a while. The old wing was seldom used.

But it was in use now, for Countess Moira had chosen the huge bedroom with its sweeping view of Lough Allen and the Dowra Mountains, cradling the source of the River Shannon. Often as a child she had used the red and silver room, with its huge red-canopied bed, for a playroom. During this visit, she had installed the children in her old lavender and white room at the end of the passage, she and her husband occupying the room always referred to as 'The Room With the View.'

The storm continued unabated. The fury of the wind seemed to increase. Grandfather Considine made jokes about the old Ark, as the house wrenched at every blast of wind.

After dinner on the second day of this demented weather, Count Sczriny said the dampness had clutched at his throat all day. He would go to bed with camphor flannel wrapped around his throat, so that he would feel quite fit to start for Paris the next day.

Always after dinner, Peter and Maria joined their grandmother and grandfather in the library to listen to the stories of Gaelic deeds, ancient as the Mountains of Dowra, and as magic. Tonight, after making sure her husband was tucked comfortably in bed, their mother came in and sat on the hearth seat, her arm around Maria.

Just as Grandfather Considine was reaching the end of the story of Grain O'Nalley, the wondrous pirate queen of the isles, Peter Sczriny's arm shot out, pointing at the wall across from the fireplace where they were sitting. 'Mother, look, the wall is wet. It looks like big tears. Mother, what is it?'

Every head turned. Then no one moved. No one spoke. In the tense stillness, the watchers saw a web of water spread across the grey wall. A large map of hunting coverts, insecurely tacked to the wall, bulged with moisture, sagged, and fell with a plop to the floor.

Then, slowly, inexorably, the unseen fingers wrote the letters A-L-E-X-A-N-D-E-R, Peter spelled out the word 'Alexander', Maria repeated it. These two unhappy children saw the written but quickly obliterated name of their father, for they had Sczriny blood fused with that of Considine. To them the name stood out bold and bright.

The three others, being Considines, saw the writing only dimly through the moisture that stained the grey painted wall as it wept.

The full import of what this meant spread slowly in the mind of the countess. She sprang up from the bench where she had been sitting. 'This is impossible,' she cried. 'Alex is not away from home, he is asleep upstairs. It always happens to a Sczriny who is away from his house. He is safe, safe,' and she ran out of the room and started to mount the stairs.

A gigantic blast of wind struck the embattled old house of Drumshambo amidships, followed immediately by a crash of rending wood. The impact of wind and the crash above almost

23

floored the five persons trying to crowd past each other on the stairs. Young Peter reached the door of the Red Chamber first. He threw open the door. Behind him grouped his mother and sister and his grandparents. The sight they saw was almost too heartbreaking to bear. Long-neglected old stonework had not withstood the impact of Atlantic gales of the past two days. A massive chimney, built when Charles Stuart ruled England, had crashed down, carrying the rotting timbers and broken tiles of the roof with it. Down it had hurtled through the ceiling and bed canopy, crushing the life out of Count Alexander Sczriny, who lay half buried under soaking timbers and rubble. Through the gaping hole in the roof, storm clouds ripped away from a wan moon; the storm was over.

A few days later, a long letter arrived from Poland. The mother of little Stephan, the child who had been savaged by a stallion many years ago, now lived at Castle Sczriny, a very old woman, nearing ninety.

In this letter, the old countess told how she had been sitting in the room across from the Green Salon on the night of the fatal storm on Lough Allen, the same room in which she had taken tea that afternoon, so many years ago, when, looking up from her embroidery, she had seen the wall weep, and, horrified, had watched the finger write the name of her adored small son, Stephan.

This time the wall in the Green Salon had run dark with water, and for twenty minutes the cascades slanted and wavered as if blown by a high wind. The name Alexander appeared for an instant, then faded away in tears. It had seemed odd to her, she remembered, that, although her eyesight was impaired by her great age, the writing on the wall appeared crystal clear.

Later, when notes were compared, it was found the wall at Castle Sczriny wept at nine minutes past ten o'clock, the wall at Drumshambo, at ten o'clock.

Count Peter Sczriny somehow escaped the curse, but it struck again in 1940 when his nineteen-year-old son Count Casimir Sczriny was killed in an aeroplane accident in the Carpathian Mountains.

This time, the walls at both Castle Sczriny and Drumshambo wept the night before the accident. Since Castle Sczriny was then a headquarters for a field-marshal of the Third Reich, those who saw the wall weep did not see the name appear upon it.

At Drumshambo, an elderly man lay crippled by age in an upper chamber. Only servants saw the wall weep. A dampness rose up from the floor, quenching the fire in the grate and causing a smudge to drift through the house. No name was seen.

As recently as 1943 the grey wall in the shuttered library at Drumshambo dripped tears, for a much longer time than ever before, it is said, and a dampness pervaded the room for days. As no word of any kind has been heard from a member of the Sczriny-Oransky family since the end of World War II, it is not known where the curse of Sczriny struck.

RATHLIN ISLAND

There is an old ruin called Bruce's Castle on this island, and the legend runs that Bruce and his chief warriors lie in an enchanted sleep in a cave of the rock on which stands the castle, and that one day they will rise up and unite the island to Scotland.

The entrance to this cave is visible only once in seven years. A man who happened to be travelling by at the time discovered it, and entering in he found himself all at once in the midst of the heavy-handed warriors. He looked down and saw a sabre half-unsheathed in the earth at his feet, and on his attempting to draw it every man of the sleepers lifted up his head and put his hand on his sword. The man being much alarmed fled from the cave, but he heard voices calling fiercely after him: 'Ugh! ugh! Why could we not be left to sleep?' And they clanged their swords on the ground with a terrible noise, and then all was still, and the gate of the cave closed with a mighty sound like a clap of thunder.

THE RAID
SEAN O'CASEY

The cold beauty of frost glittered everywhere outside, unseen, unfelt, for the slum was asleep. An uneasy silence echoed over the house, for awake or asleep, everyone knew that death with his comrade, the inflictor of wounds, roamed the darkened streets. Stretched out in a truckle bed in a tenement room, its murky window facing on to the street, Sean thought of the tapestry of the day. He could see the street stretching along outside, its roughly cobbled roadway beset with empty matchboxes, tattered straws, tattered papers, scattered mounds of horse-dung, and sprinkled deep with slumbering dust waiting for an idle wind to come and raise it to irritating life again. Lean-looking gas-lamps stood at regular intervals on the foot-paths, many of them deformed from the play of swinging children, bending over like old men standing to gasp, and wait for a pain in the back to go. The melancholy pathway meandered along by the side of the tall houses, leading everywhere to tarnishing labour, to consumption's cough, to the writhings of fever, to bitter mutterings against life, and frantic calls on St Anthony, The Little Flower, and Bernadette of Missabielle to be absent helps in time of trouble. Upon these stones, I will build my church.

There were the houses, too—a long, lurching row of discontented incurables, smirched with the age-long marks of ague, fevers, cancer, and consumption, the soured tears of little children, and the sighs of disappointed newly-married girls. The doors were scarred with time's spit and anger's hasty knocking; the pillars by their sides were shaky, their stuccoed bloom long since peeled away, and they looked like crutches keeping the trembling doors standing on their palsied feet. The gummy-eyed windows blinked dimly out, lacquered by a year's tired dust from the troubled street below. Dirt and disease were the big sacraments here—outward and visible signs of an inward and spiritual disgrace. The people bought the cheapest things in food they could find in order to live, to work, to worship: the cheapest spuds, the cheapest tea, the cheapest meat, the cheapest fat; and waited for unsold bread to grow stale that they might buy that cheaper, too. Here they gathered up the fragments so that nothing would be lost. The streets were long haggard corridors of rottenness and ruin. What wonderful mind of memory could link this shrinking wretchedness with the flaunting gorgeousness of silk and satin; with bloom of rose and scent of lavender? A thousand years must have passed since the last lavender lady was carried out feet first from the last surviving one of them. Even the sun shudders now when she touches a roof, for she feels some evil has chilled the glow of her garment. The flower that here once bloomed is dead forever. No wallflower here has crept into a favoured cranny; sight and sign of the primrose were far away; no room here for a dance of daffodils; no swallow twittering under a shady eave; and it was sad to see an odd sparrow seeking a yellow grain from the mocking dust; not even a spiky-headed thistle, purple mitred, could find a corner here for a sturdy life. No Wordsworth here wandered about as lonely as a cloud.

> The decent dead provoke no blood-congealing fear,
> Like the dread death that lives to fester here.
> Here children, lost to every sense but life,
> Indulge in play that mimics social strife;
> And learn from strenuous practice that they may
> Act well their part at home some future day:
> The girl trains her lungs to scream and shout,
> The boy his arms to knock a wife about.

And yet his riddled horridness has given root to the passion flower. What has been lost was found; what has been dead came to life again. The spirit beneath the coat brocaded, with slender sword quivering, had come into being again, not in brocade, but in rags; not with sword or dainty phrases, elegant in comedy and satire; but with bitter curses, blows as hard as an arm can give, and a rank, savage spit into a master's face. Fought these frantic fools did, led by Larkin and by Connolly; fought till the day-star arose in their shivering hearts, the new and glorious light, the red evangel, the light of the knowledge of the glory of God, manifested in the active mind and vital bodies of men and women and little children. And now something stronger than bare hands was in the battle. Many a spearpoint flame from a gun frightened a dark corner or a shadowy street, making armed men in khaki or black crouch low in their rushing lorries, firing rapidly back at the street grown shadowy again, or the corner now darker than ever before.

Now the old house was still. Comely Bessie Ballynoy, on her way up, had knocked; but finding Seán in bed, had bid good-night, and gone. Lazy sleep had crawled in by the dark hallway to soothe restlessness and to hush the clamour from the attic above to the basement below. A lousy sleep, dreary-eyed, in loosely slippered feet, torn and muddy, calling in a shoddy whisper for quietness; creeping in yawning, leaving no-one on watch, though every night now was a perilous night for Dublin. In all the rooms, all the cheap crockery stood quiet on the shelves; the chairs leaned against the shaky walls; rosy-faced fires had all gone pale; the patter of children's feet had long since ceased; only dreams crept slyly in to fill the ugly rooms with sparkling peace for a few dark moments, clothing the sleepers with a cautious splendour; setting them, maybe, to sip rare wines from bulging bottles, or led them to yellow sands bordering a playful sea. A younger lass, perhaps, dreamed of scanty night attire between snowy sheets, with a colour-robed prince by the bedroom door in haste to come in, and bid her a choice goodnight; while the younger men saw themselves, sword in hand, driving the khaki cut-throats out of Eire's five beautiful fields.

Every guardian angel relaxed now, and nodded sleepily by tattered counterpane and ragged sheet, for sin usually curled up like a dog to sleep at their feet waiting for the tenement life to go on again in the morning. So after Curfew the silent tenement slept, unconscious even that every whining wail of every passing motor sang a song of death to someone; for in sleep the slimy roof above them had slid aside, and left the stars but a hand's breadth out of reach.

When will the day break in Eirinn; when will her day-star arise? How often had he heard these words sung in a languishing voice after an eight-hand reel or a high-cauled cap at ceilidh or *sgoruidheacht*! Well, no day would ever break here, nor would the shadows ever flee away. Sean's eyes were closing, and dimming thoughts swooned faintly from his mind into the humming whine of motor-engines coming quick along the road outside. Up on his elbow he shot as he heard the sound of braking, telling him that the lorries were outside of his house, or of those on either side. Then he shot down again to hide as a blinding beam from a searchlight poured through the window, skimming the cream of the darkness out of the room. It silvered the old walls for a few moments, then withdrew like a receding tide to send its beam on another part of the house. Then there was a volley of battering blows on the obstinate wooden door, mingled with the crash of falling glass that told Sean the panels on each side of it had been shattered by hammer or rifle-butt.

A raid! All the winsome dreams of the house had vanished; sleep had gone; and children dug arms and legs into the tensing bodies of their mothers.

Which were they—the Tommies or the Tans? Tans, thought Sean, for the Tommies would not shout so soullessly, nor smash the glass panels so suddenly; they would hammer on the door with a rifle-butt and wait for it to be opened.

No; these were the Tans.

He heard the quick pit-put, pit-put of stockinged feet, faint as it was, coming down the stairs, turning left at the bottom of them, and hurrying along the hall towards the back-yard. His ears were so cocked that he heard the soft, silky pad of the hurrying feet plainly through the storm of blows falling on the street door; then he thought he heard the back door open softly and gently close again.

Who could that be? he thought. Might be any one of the men. Those who didn't take part in ambushes often carried ammunition to those who did; and the dockers and seamen gave a ready hand to the smuggling in of arms. If it wasn't for his own poor sight, he'd probably be doing it himself. All were friendly, save the thin and delicate husband of Mrs

30

Ballynoy, who cared for no manner of politics. Someone, anyway, slipping into the back to dodge over the wall into the dark lanes, with fear but without fuss. The Dublin slums at war with the British Empire; all the power of an army, flanked by gangs of ruthless ruffians; all the ordered honour of a regal cabinet and the mighty-moneyed banks fighting the ragged tits of the tenements. An unequal fight, by God, but the slums would win.

There goes the door!

A great crash shook the old house and shook the heart of Sean, for well he knew the ordeal that might be in front of him once the light from a Tan's torch smote the darkness of the room. A mad rush of heavy feet went past his door, to spread over the stilly house; for no-one had come from a room to risk sudden death in the dark and draughty hallway. He remembered the two boys brought bound from Dublin Castle to a dump-field on the edge of the city by two Auxie-tan officers, who set them sitting against an old stone wall, extinguishing each young head under an old bucket picked from a rubbish heap. Then going away forty paces or so, they fired away at the buckets till they were full of holes, leaving what they had done behind them to put the fear of the Tans into the hearts of the surviving IRA men. He thought, too, of Clancy, Clune, and McKee, caught and brought to the Castle, where the Tans interviewed them with the stimulant of bayonets, prodding them gamely till none of the three could sigh any longer, for each at last was dead. Now he could hear neither sound nor murmur—all had gone quiet after the crashing fall of the door. No sound even of a child's protest, though that wasn't surprising, for all of them would be too frightened to squeal till a gun exploded somewhere: all was quiet—the sad silence of a sleeping slum. Yet Sean knew that the house must be alive with crawling men, slinking up and down the stairs, hovering outside this door or that one, each with a gun tensed to the last hair, with a ready finger touching the trigger. He guessed that a part of them were the Auxies, the classic members of sibilant and sinister raiders. The Tans alone would make more noise, slamming themselves into a room, shouting to shake off the fear that

slashed many of their faces. The Auxies were too proud
to show a sign of it. The Tommies would be warm, always
hesitant at knocking a woman's room about; they would even
be jocular in their funny English way, encouraging the women
and even the children to grumble at being taken away from
their proper sleep.

All Sean could do was to try to lie dead still, digging down
deeper without a sound into the hard mattress of his truckle
bed; stifling any desire to steal to the door to listen; to try to
modify his breathing till it became unnoticed by himself; for
a profound silence might make the Tans disinclined to probe
a way in to find out the cause of it; though the Auxies cared
nothing for silence, but would lift a corpse from a coffin to
search for a gun. He always left his door unlocked now, for
past experience had shown him that the slightest obstacle to a
swift entrance to a room always irritated them.

From the corner of an eye he could see through the window
the searchlight gliding, now up, now down the street, and
once for a few moments it blinded him by flooding the room.
Then he heard sullen, but loud, thuds of heavy iron falling
on heavy wood, coming from the back, and he guessed they
were breaking in the entrance to the large shed that was said
to be used as a carpenter's shop, and in which Mrs Ballynoy's
husband sometimes worked. Now he heard soft, sly steps
going down the hallway to the back. After whomsoever had
crept away while the door was being broken down. He had
climbed the wall, thought Sean, and somewhere—maybe just
behind it—crouched silently in the darkest corner of the
narrow lane, a revolver tight in his hand, his shoes slung round
his neck, so that, if he had to run, no sound of running
feet would give an enemy a cue of a direction through which
to send a hail of bullets; a bitter night for a pair of bare feet.

Sean could sense the women, and, maybe, the men, praying
while the hammering lasted, to cease at once when silence
came again, for it wouldn't serve them to let the Auxies
hear them trying to talk to God. These silences were the
worst; during the hammering one knew where they were;
throughout the silences one didn't. Then they might be any-
where; might be opening his very own door snakily, softly,

now; some of them might be even in the room, for their black uniforms fitted the darkness they loved, and black juices, smeared over their cheeks and brows, mixed them cosily with the darker shadows of the night. Any moment a brilliant torch might blind his slatted eyes, and a string of shouted questions blast his ear; a pressed-in, cold pistol barrel make a tiny livid rim on his naked chest. He tried to forget thought, making his mind one with the darkness, losing his fear in the vastness of space; but it was no use, for thought never got farther than that the Tans were there, and his mind came back to think of how it would feel to have a bullet burning a swift channel through the middle of his belly.

Azrael. Azrael, gentle, dignified being of spirit, graceful spirit of death, come, and minister unto us, and save us merry gentlemen.

> Come lovely and soothing death,
> Undulate round the world, serenely arriving,
> Arriving
> In the day, In the night, to all, to each,
> Sooner or later, delicate death.

Ah! Whitman, Walt Whitman, you never knew the Tans. Death doesn't arrive serenely here, his hands are desperate, and neither is he delicately formed. Here the angel of death is a biting bitch!

The silence was startled by the sound of a motor-engine warming up, getting ready to go. He heard steps now in the hall, and the sound of bravura jests from a few voices. They were going. They mightn't be, though: they pretended that at times, driving the lorries away a bit, but leaving the men, behind, to come with a rush into the house again among foolish people hurrying in their nightclothes out of their rooms to ask questions of each other. Stay still; don't move; not a stir; some of them still might be just beyond the door.

He lay there for what seemed a long time, the sweat of fear damping his body, and making him shiver. Stay still; don't move—someone was beside the door. He heard the handle giving a faint, brassy murmur. Soon, a black-clothed arm would thrust itself within, and a shot might go off that he would never hear. He silently squirmed deeper into the bed, and left the rest to God.

Eh! he heard the voice of Mrs Ballynoy whisper from the darkness, Are you there, or did they take you? Are you gone, or · are you asleep, or wha'?

That woman again! he thought resentfully—what a fright she gave me! Awake, Mrs Ballynoy, he whispered back.

Well, she said softly, you can take your ayse now, an' sleep tranquil, or get up, an' talk about th' queer things done in a Christian age.

Wait till I light a candle, he said, making a great creak as he heaved himself out of the bed's hollow.

You'll light no candle while I'm here, young man, said her voice, dressed in a titter, for a slip of overall's th' only shelter between me and a piercin' look from a young man's eyes; an' it wouldn't be good to go from one extreme to another on an identical night.

Did they discover anything? asked Sean.

Not a thing, though they took two o' th' men away with them. A sudden end to them all, an' a short fall to th' hottest hob that hell can heat! Don't light that candle yet, she added, for minds that have safely passed a danger near them are often reckless in their dealin' with an innocent female; though you're not that kind of a man, I know.

He heard the door softly closing and her hand fumbling with the lock. He hoped she wasn't going to stay. Ah! here's the key, for it's safer to put a locked door between eyes that pry into other people's affairs day an' night, tintin' everything with the colour of their own minds.

Hadn't you better go back to your room, Mrs Ballynoy, he warned. You need all the sleep you can get these days. We all do; and someone might be prowlin' round and see an' think th' worst.

Ay, she said; bad minds, th' lot o' them—that's why I've locked the door. An' call me Nellie, for you know me well enough be now. Light th' candle now you can, but leave it on th' far side of where I'll be, for it's only a flimsy apron-overall I have between me an' all harm; and she tittered gaily as Sean very slowly lighted a candle on a box beside his bed.

She was a fine-looking heifer, right enough: long reddish hair coiled up into a bunch that rested neatly on the nape of a white neck; a well-chiselled, pale face, with large grey innocent eyes that seemed to be shrouded in a mist from the valley of the Missabielle; a fine figure set these charms off, and when she slyly waved this sweet figure in front of a man, he no longer saw, or wanted to see, the mist of Missabielle. A rose of Tralee, without the flower's serenity, maybe; but certainly a lovely rose of the tenements. But Sean was in no mood now to enjoy the charm of her fine figure and face. Once let a soul see she had been in his room and the whole house would be declaring that he was carrying on with Mrs Bally-noy. He should have had the courage to get up and push her out. He almost wished now that the Auxies had stayed a little longer.

In the sober light of the candle he saw that she had just decorated her delightful body in a pair of brown slippers and a flowered overall reaching only half-way down her thighs, and showing a wide part of her white swelling bosom; a show that was very charming, but damned uncomfortable to one who was determined to take no notice of it.

Oh! There ye'are, she said, when the candle-light got steady, nice an' snug an' all alone. She came over and sat down on the edge of the bed beside him. I'm asking meself why a land, overflowin' with prayer an' devotion, should be so often plunged into dhread in the dead o' night for nothin'? An' they tellin' me it's for Ireland's sake. Them politics'll be the death of us some day. I feel terrible shy in this get-up, she said suddenly. Afther washin' the one good nightgown I have, I was sleepin' in me skin, an' this overall was th 'first thing I laid hands on when the Tans came thundherin' at the door. Pansies on it, she said, giggling, pulling it a little from her thigh, pansies for thought! and she poked Sean in the breast, playfully, with a hand reddened by the soda she used in the washing of clothes.

Isn't Mr Ballynoy at home, said Sean, trying to get her mind away from the overall, while he thought of a way to get rid of her.

Didn't I tell you this mornin', on the stairs, that he was on a counthry job! He would be when the Tans come; though it's little good he'd be in any emergency, bein' born timid, with a daisy in his mouth. So I'm a poor lone lassie now, and she gave him another poke—this time in the thigh.

Don't you think you ought to get back, he warned; the Tans might come again.

Ay, indeed, they might; a body can never know what them fellas'll do. An' it only a little way from Christmas, too. Ah! she said suddenly, looking away into a dream distance; it's good to be near one of your own: th' only two protestants in th' house, not countin' me husband. Of the crowd, not countin' him, only two who have th' proper way o' worshippin' an' are able to forsee th' genuine meanin' of th' holy text.

There's me for you, said Sean, thinking neither you nor your husband bothered about religion, one way or another.

Then you're sadly mistaken. I can't remember a year we missed feelin' the curious chantin' glow in th' air of a Christmas mornin', an' us on our way to church. In a proper mood, an' that was often, I could see what you'd think's th' star, ashine on the tip of the spire's top; an' me ears can hear th' dull plod of the three camels' feet in th' deep sand, bearin' th' three kings with th' three rich gifts from Persia, or some other place in th' wilds of a far away world; an' all th' time an anxious man seekin' shelter for his good woman, with the valleys levelled an' th' hills hidden be th' fallin' snow, dyein' her rich hair grey with its fallin' flakes, a sly soft carpet for her sandalled feet, and sore they were from th' sting in its frosty tendherness; while th' tired Joseph thrudged demented behind, wondherin' if they'd find their lodgins only on the cowld, cowld ground. But God was good, an' found the shelther of a stable for the bewildhered, half perished man, with his thin gown sodden, his toil-marked hands a hot ache, an' his poor feet blue with the bitther penetration of th' clingin' snow; an' afther Joseph has shooed th' puzzled animals to a safe an' ordherly distance, th' little fella was soon snug in a manger on top o' warm heaps of sainfoin, thyme, rosemary, an' lavender.

You're wrong there, said Sean; for how in such a bitther season could anyone come on spring and summer plants like those?

I dunno, she murmured, unless God turned th' hay an' th' straw into th' sweet-savourin' herbs. But it's far betther not to thry to go into them things. Are you afraid to look at me or what? she ejaculated, turning away from her dreams; for Sean had turned his head away to escape the charm of the white bosom and soft thighs. As long as you don't make too free, I don't mind, though I feel a little shy in this scarce get-up.

A shoulder-band of the overall had slipped down, and she had saucily drawn an arm out of it altogether so that near half of her body to the waist was bare, and he saw a breast, rather lovely in the light of the candle, looking like a golden cup with a misty ruby in its centre. If he only had her in a shady corner of the Phoenix Park, or in a room of his own in a house where she wasn't known, the world would be well lost for a period of ecstasy. But not here.

Your husband's a good fellow, he said trying to keep his mind off her, and would rejoice to see you as you are now. He thinks a lot of you.

He oughtn't, she said sarcastically; where'd he get another like me? He means well, poor man, but honest, it's pathetic when we're alone an' he thries to get goin'. Askin' me to tell him when he's hurtin' me! She went into a soft, gay, gurgling laugh, putting a hand over her mouth to quench the merry sound of it. It's funny to talk of it here, but maddenin' when I'm with him. I'm often near worn out thryin', thryin' to coax a little flash of endeavour outa him. He does his best, but the little sting he once had's gone with the wind—joy go with it! She now laughed venomously and loud, making Sean fearful of someone hearing her. Wait till I tell you, she went on—you'll die laughin'! You should see Charlie when he's at the he-man business—are you sure you won't get faint, Nellie? Don't forget to say if I'm hurtin' you, dearie! One night, when he was—you know—I jerked him clean outa th' bed on to th' floor—th' bump shook th' house! D'ye know, honest t'God, he just lay stunned there. Put th' heart across me. Ever afther, d'ye know, I've had to handle him like a delicate piece of china! No; poor Charlie's style's too shy for me. Not like Jim Achree's. J'ever hear o' his?

She slid down till she was half lying over him, and sang sedulously beside his ear:

> Jim Achree's style has a wonderful way with it,
> All th' girls' minds are in sad disarray with it;
> Whenever they venture to have a short play with it,
> Good girls want to stay with it, ever an' aye.
> Oh! Jim Achree, shure your style is your own,
> Amazin' th' way it has flourished and grown,
> With lovely threats shakin', tense with mischief makin'
> Knockin' poor woman flat like a gorgeous cyclone.

Looka, she said breathlessly, th' least bit o' fondlin' now, an' I'd swoon away, helpless an' benighted.

In the midst of death we are in life, thought Sean. He tried to turn his head away so that he wouldn't be prompted by the white breast that was like a golden cup with a misty ruby in its centre; but his head refused to stir. Instead, he found his hand sliding over her fair bosom. He felt her arm pushing away under his head till it was firmly round his neck, while the other pushed the clothes from covering him. He was lost, unless he yelled for help, and that he couldn't do.

You're a good young man, he heard her whispering, an' would never take advantage of a woman alone in your room in th' dead o' night, with but a loose slip between you an' a swift lie-down on a bed o' meadow-sweet. Don't sthruggle, man, or you'll upset things. Why'r you thryin' to keep me from gettin' the clothes down? You've far too many on you; a little cool air'll do you good. Take th' good things while they're goin'. She whipped the clothes down with a fierce jerk, and lying beside him, pressed her mouth to his. Her big innocent eyes looked frantic now.

G'won, she muttered, panting, be as rough as you like with

me—it's what I'm longin' for for weeks. And half mad himself now, he gripped her like a vice, and sank his fingers into her flesh.

Then they suddenly went still as death, listening; listening to the whine of a motor-engine cruising down the road outside. Then another whine followed that, and another, the last, till they mingled into one shrill, threatening whine that went echoing round the walls of the old house.

Out in strength tonight, thought Sean; more'n three of them; each of them crooning a song of death to someone. Ireland's modern, senseless Banshee.

Suddenly the shrill whine lifted into a shrill, quavering scream, the scream fading into the throb, throb of active engines as the lorries stopped outside, or very near, the house.

They've stopped at this house, or th' next one! said Nellie, loosening her arm from around his neck, and sliding swift from the bed to the door. Who' ha' thought th' bastards would bother to come twice th' same night? Christ? It's this house they're makin' for! And swiftly came a great hammering on the door again. Nellie frantically twisted and turned at the key, but she couldn't get the door of the room open.

In they'll come, she squealed softly, an' I'll be exposed to th' world as a fast woman. She tugged and writhed till the slip fell from her shoulders, leaving her naked, fuming, at the door. You it was, she half-shouted, turning a red and bitter face towards Sean, that lured me into this predicament, never able to let any decent woman pass without thryin' to meddle her!

Sean as eager as she was herself that she should go unseen, leaped out of bed, hurried over, and with a hard twist, turned the key. Snatching up her flowered overall, she whipped the door open, rushed out, and up the stairs, without another word. Shutting the door again, he fled back to bed, digging himself down deep into it once again, listening to hear if it was Tan or Tommy who had entered the house.

The door spun open, and a torchlight shot terror into his eyes. Silently he waited for a blow or a shot, but neither came. He opened his eyes, and say a young Khaki-clad officer just inside the door, a torch in one hand, a revolver in the other. Behind him were two soldiers with rifles at ready. The officer stared at Sean, then slowly returned the gun to a holster, and the soldiers, at this sign, stood at ease, and rested the butts of the rifles on the dirty floor.

Get up; dress; go out to the street, said the officer tersely; this house has to be searched room by room. Don't try to go farther than the wire cordon ringing the district; orders are to fire on any who do. He watched Sean dressing, and when he saw him clap a cap on his head, asked, Haven't you an overcoat?

A sort of a one, said Sean.

Better than nothing; you'd better put it on—it's damned cold outside.

Decent man, thought Sean, putting on his old coat; has an occasional thought for others. Thank God, the Tans are absent!

He went out into the dark hall, and near bumped into a Tan standing there, fingering a heavy revolver. A cold shiver trickled down his spine.

Where are you going? he asked.

Outside to street—officer's orders, said Sean.

What officer? asked the Tan.

Military officer, sir.

Oh! Military officer, eh? Well, we give the orders here—understand?

Yessir, said Sean promptly.

Are you a Sinn Feiner? he questioned, twisting the gun in his hand.

A Sinn Feiner? Me? No fear.

You were one, then.

No; never, said Sean emphatically. Thank God, thought Sean, he didn't ask if I had ever been a Republican. The ignorant English bastard doesn't know the difference.

Well, you're an Irishman, anyway—you can't deny that!

No sir, I can't deny that I'm an Irishman, right enough.

Well, shout To Hell with Ireland, and you can go—no mutter, but a shout the house can hear. Now!

But Sean fell silent. God damn him if he'd do that! He knew his face was white; he felt his legs tremble; but he fell silent, with a stubborn look on his face.

Go on, you Sinn Fein rat, shout it!

A streak of light fell on them, and Sean saw the young officer coming to them. He stopped, looked at Sean, then looked at the Tan.

What's wrong here? he asked. Let that man go into the street.

You mind your own damned business, snarled the Tan.

I am minding it, said the young officer. I happen to be an Irishman, too. Have you any objection to it?

I don't take orders from you! said the Tan roughly.

I'm not sorry for that, the officer said; but this man does —didn't I give you an order to go into the street? he asked, turning to Sean.

Yessir.

Carry it out, then, he said sharply; and Sean, turning swiftly, made a quick march through the hall, out by the door, into the street.

It was very cold, and from the timid gleams from a waning moon, Sean saw the path and road were white with a covering of rich rime frost. Groups of people were standing, huddled up against the railings of the houses, while more were oozing sleepily out of the remaining ones, shepherded into bunches by armed soldiers. The women were trying to coax warmth into their tearful and shivering children by wrapping flimsy rags round their shoulders, and tucking the little ones under them into their arms.

Several searchlights wandered through the street, flashing over the groups of people, or tinselling along the walls of the houses. At one end stood an armoured car, the lids raised, showing the heads of several Tommies who were quietly chanting an advice to the shivering people to pack up their troubles in their old kit-bags. Along the road, over the calm, quiet chastity of the white frost, slid a diamond-shaped tank, looking like a dirty, dangerous crawling slug, machine-guns sticking out from slits, like ugly protruding eyes staring at the cowering people.

He saw a commotion round the door of the house, he lived in. He mooched over till he was beside the steps to look over the shoulders of a rank of soldiers. A prisoner! Who could it be? He whisperingly asked the soldier in front of him what had happened.

An awrsenal! whispered the soldier hoarsely. Rear of th' 'ouse, an awrsenal discovered! 'Nough gelignite to blow up 'ole neighbourhood. A blighter there drew a gun, but was shot through hand afore'ee could pull trigger. 'Ere's the bawstard coming.

Amid a group of soldiers with rifles at the ready marched a thin forlorn figure, but the lips in the pale face were tight together, and the small head was held high. Peering closer, Sean saw the handcuffs kept the two small hands locked together, and that from one of them red blobs were dripping on to the white frost on the path, leaving little spots behind like crimson berries that had fallen on to snow. In the hall he heard the voice of Nellie shouting.

That's me husband! he heard her shout; a good man an' a brave one! Yous'll never shoot the life outa Ireland, yous gang o' armed ruffians! Here, take me, too, if yous aren't afraid. Keep your pecker up, Charlie—Ireland's with you!

Sean peered closer, Good God—the prisoner was the timid insignificant Charlie Ballynoy who took no interest in politics! A lorry, full of soldiers, swirled into the kerb. The handcuffed prisoner was pushed and lifted into it. Standing there in the middle of the soldiers, with the searchlight covering him with glory, he held up his iron-locked hands from which clouts of blood still dripped.

Up the Republic! he shouted with the full force of his voice.

The lorry drove off, and the red specks in the rime turned brown and lonely. Heads that had lifted bent again, and all was quiet once more. A bleak dawn at last began to peel the deeper darkness from the sky, and the scene crept into a ghostly glamour, brightened by the pale faces of the waiting people; the pale moon sinking deeper into a surly sky, and the rimy frost on pathways, road, and roof grew whiter. Dirty-yellow-clad figures moved into the whiteness from one dark doorway, to move out of it again into another blacker still: while the brown, slug-like tank crept up and down the road, charring the dainty rime with its grinding treads—the new leviathan that God could ne'er control.

DEATH SIGNS

In one Irish family a cuckoo always appears before a death. A lady who arrived on a visit at a house observed one morning a cuckoo perched on the window-sill, but she felt no alarm, for there was no sickness in the family. Next day, however, one of the sons was carried home dead. He had been thrown from his horse when hunting, and killed on the spot.

In another family a mysterious sound is heard like the crashing of boards, and a rush of wind seems to pass through the house, yet nothing is broken or disturbed. The death of an officer in the Crimea was in this way announced to his family, for the news came immediately after the warning sound, and then they knew that the rush of the wind was the spirit of the dead which had passed by them, but without taking any visible form.

THE WARNING
PATRICK BARDAN

Bryan Maguire was the son of a prosperous farmer who resided within a short distance of the town of Moate. From early childhood his love for books predominated over all the allurements of his class; and his simple-minded parents, believing that they saw in his studious habits and subdued or melancholy demeanour, unmistakable proof that he was predestined for the sacred ministry, settled it quietly between themselves that Bryan should be sent to college, and accordingly he was packed off to a distant seminary where he was forced to undergo a course of study not at all to his liking; and when at the mature age of twenty-one he quitted it to enter the famous establishment of Maynooth, he felt inwardly convinced that he had no vocation for the priesthood, and that in offering himself as a candidate for orders he was complying with the will of his parents—not his own. On the day preceding his intended departure he strolled over his father's extensive farm intent on bidding a final farewell to all the familiar scenes of his childhood. It was the beautiful Maytime, when nature was dressed in her richest garb; but Bryan Maguire was too much absorbed in his own thoughts to derive any pleasure from the contemplation of the scenic charms aroundhim.

His walk led him to a spring well that bubbled from beneath a rock in a secluded dale, and over which a flowering hawthorn threw its grateful shade. This well had the reputation of being a 'holy' one, and the surrounding peasantry were accustomed to make stations in the early Autumn. Bryan was in the act of carving his initials on the back of the ancient hawthorn when a slight noise behind him attracted his attention. Glancing in that direction he saw a female figure. It was Winnie Byrne, the daughter of one of his father's cottiers, who had come for a pitcher of water. Winnie, though rather plump of figure possessed a face of considerable attractions, albeit a heavy frown habitually lingered about her sloe-black eyes. As it happened

45

that she and Bryan Maguire had not met for several years it is not surprising that he failed to recognise her at first sight; but immediately on his recovering from the slight surprise which her unexpected presence occasioned, he advanced towards her with outstretched hand, cheerily remarking: 'Winnie Byrne, by all that's good! How you have grown out of my knowledge, Winnie, since you and I were young!' 'Oh, thank you, Mr Maguire. It's little thought ever you gave to the like of me while you had grand people to speak to. But is it true that you are going away to-morrow?' 'It is true, then, Winnie. Permit me to quaff a draught from your pitcher. Well, to be sure, what a fine girl you have grown!' 'And, Mr Maguire'—pretending not to have heard his remark about herself—'do you pay no heed to what the saint who caused this well to spring forth, and blessed it for the poor people? Didn't he lay his curse on the *shoneens* of the parish, and predict that no native of it would ever be called to the priesthood?'

'I have certainly heard of the strange malediction,' answered Bryan, 'but I do not know that it has ever yet been put to the test; I suppose that ordeal is reserved for me.' He tried to laugh, but the serious look in the young girl's face prevented him, 'He should be greater than the saint who could do that; besides, something tells me you were not born to fill that high station; you may become great in the other walks of life—but the bells of glory will never ring while you read the Gospel of our holy Church.' 'Well, now, Winnie, I did not think you were such a speaker!—a prophetess, in fact. But I hope you have not been taking lessons from old Sinead the sybil, that lives up in the hills yonder?' He laughed heartily at what he considered his own natural wit, and failed to notice the momentary blanching of Winnie's cheek as she marked his observation. In the confusion of the moment she felt at a loss for a reply, and Bryan continued in the same light tone: 'You know Sinead can work both good and evil for the *colleens*, but won't lift a finger for the boys—at least so I am told.' 'It matters not,' observed the maiden, testily, 'if you are determined to go on your course, though—if I may make so bold—maybe you would regret it when too late, and feel that you had missed your vocation in not pursuing the life of an honest farmer with some handsome *colleen* for a wife, who would love you and serve you through every change of fortune.' The damsel assumed a dramatic *pose* as she spoke these words; her face glistened like diamonds. Even the ascetic student was visibly affected as he gazed upon her form and noted the earnestness of her appeal. 'Perhaps you are right, Winnie. I think I see plainly that I *have* missed my vocation, and it is passing strange how you have been the first to point it out to me. For the future you will have more interest in my eyes than any other female of my acquaintance. Hear me now, Winnie'—he took her hand in his and looked wistfully into her flashing eyes—'you have kindled an unwonted flame within my bosom, and it is for you to encourage it or not. I will leave the dangerous path I have been treading; I will brave the reproaches of parents and friends, as well as the sneers of my enemies if you will consent to share my—love! Speak, Winnie, and make me happy or miserable by your decision.' 'Bryan, you surprise me very much, and perhaps I have spoken too rashly, but—but—my feelings prompted me to speak so.'

Here she appeared totally overpowered by emotion, and it was not until the love-smitten student had fondled her in his arms like a pettish child that she was able to proceed. At length, laying her head on his breast she resumed; 'I have loved you secretly since we were children, Bryan, but was always too shy to confess it before you. However, it may be Heaven's will to bring us together in this way; and if you will be true to your own little Winnie you need never fear what others say. I have a ring about me at present, Bryan, which I will give to you as a token of my love—it is the same that my mother, and her mother before her, wore; and you will keep it while you are true to me, for young men are fickle in love affairs.' 'Do not harbour the thought, my darling Winnie, that I could act so basely,' said the infatuated young man, as he clasped her to his bosom in a paroxysm of delight. He kissed the ring with more fervour than if it was a saintly relic; and after 'many a fond and locked embrace,' he returned to his parents' domicile in that state of semi-lunacy which first love invariably produces. It is needless to describe the scene which took place when he expressed his determination to forgo the ecclesias-

tical state; enough to say that with his superior power of rea-
soning, he soon convinced them that he was right and that they
were wrong.

Next evening found Bryan Maguire at the holy well;
but it was evident that something had gone wrong with him,
for his face was ghastly pale, and a visible tremor shook
his frame. Winnie soon approached with her pitcher, and her
quick eye took in at a glance the crest-fallen appearance of her
lover; but her womanly instinct or natural cunning deterred
her from making any comment on his pallid countenance and
agitated demeanour.

'I am glad that you have been faithful to your promise,' she
observed, at the same time extending both her hands towards
him. 'I had such an ugly dream about you last night; but
dreams go by contraries, you know.' A melting glance and
fascinating smile accompanied her remark.

'It is about last night I desired to speak to you, Winnie,'
he rejoined, in a hollow voice. The artful Winnie pretended to
look scared at this, and quickly withdrew her hands from his.
'Your parents, I suppose, are against you marrying a poor
cottier's daughter, instead of choosing someone with riches and
fine clothes!'

'No, Winnie, they are yet unaware of our engagement; but—
but you knew my aunt Joanna, didn't you?' Winnie could
not gainsay the fact, for she happened to be some years older
than her refined lover.

'Well,' he resumed, 'you know she died while I was a mere
child; but I remember how she used to fondle me, and call me
her own darling *cann-a-bawn*. Last night, Winnie, I awoke out
of a light slumber and I saw her—*saw* her, Winnie, as she appeared in life, but her face was sorrowful, and the hand that she
held over me was fleshless, like that of a skeleton. "Bryan," said
she in a sepulchral voice, "you ought to give back that ring."
Just these few words, and then she disappeared from the room.'
Winnie gave vent to a sarcastic laugh. 'And so your knowledge,
Bryan, does not keep you from believing in nightmares and non-
sense. Or maybe you are satisfied with your victory over my
poor heart, and want to cast me off the first opportunity——'

'No, Winnie, I did not mean to deceive you; but what I have told you is true as that heaven is above us. My love for you remains unchanged and unalienable.'

'Then you will forgive me, Bryan, if I have spoken too rashly; for, after all, what has a poor maiden like me but her reputation.'

'And I prize you the more for guarding it, Winnie; but I fear that last night's dream does not bode good to us.'

'It was but an empty dream, Bryan, for I have often experienced such things; so let us talk no more about it. I know that your little Winnie is dearer to you than all your rich relations, and that you will yet be proud to claim her as your bride.'

Alas! it was the voice of the charmer charming wisely. Bryan Maguire had been snared in the meshes of love, and Winnie Byrne inwardly determined that he should not escape, for in securing him she saw her only chance of attaining to that position to which her heart and soul aspired.

It was midnight when a low tap sounded on the door of the hovel tenanted by Sinead the witch. 'Come in, Winnie Byrne,' said a harsh voice. The door was pushed open, and Winnie, enveloped in a heavy mantle, entered. 'Well,' said the crone, who was bending over a few embers, 'what news since I saw you last?' 'The charm done its work; Bryan Maguire, the student, drank it from my pitcher at the holy well.'

'I know—I know; but your bird is only caught, not caged. How will it be with you if he turns to another?'

The girl became deathly pale, and a baleful light flashed from her dark eyes. 'If he should—*death*!'

The summer was waning and the days began to grow shorter. It had been a long warm summer, that gave promise of a rich harvest; at least so Bryan Maguire's father averred, as he and his son sat indoors one bright afternoon discussing the prospects of the farm—a theme very irksome to Bryan, and in an equal degree congenial to his parent. The conversation was arrested by the clatter of a horse's feet and the sound of wheels on the hard dry space in front of the kitchen door, followed by the appearance of a young lady who was descending from a high gig.

'Bless me,' said the farmer, 'this is Parson Murray's daughter, I wonder what can she mean by driving here.'

But they were not long left in doubt, for Miss Murray, a lively, pleasant, and prepossessing young lady—in a few words informed them, how, being on an errand of charity, her steed grew unusually restive, so much so that her nerves began to fail her, and she deemed it prudent to seek the aid of some person able to make him tractable and drive him home. Of course the duty naturally devolved upon Bryan, who, when about to start, received instructions from his father to negotiate with the clergyman for the sale of a young ram which the farmer secretly admired.

If Bryan Maguire appeared timid and reserved at first, Miss Murray soon dispelled his reticence by alluding to topics with which he was familiar—literature, art, and science—so that before half the journey was completed he found himself deep in the mazes of a learned controversy.

The Parson received him hospitably, showed him his rare books, costly pictures, and curious antiquities—even mentioned the rare qualities of his flocks and herds, without in the least recalling to Bryan's memory the matter of his father's wish regarding the ram—so that the hours appeared to fly on angels' wings; and when Bryan bethought him of taking his leave, dinner was announced, and he was obliged to remain. After dinner the young lady was anxious to entertain him with a few national airs on the piano—he should hear her favourite, 'The Coulin,' and perhaps he might enlighten her as to its true origin, and give her much desired information on other points connected with Irish music. The good Parson fell under the spell of the melody, and snored a discordant accompaniment in his chair; some subtle influence attracted the eyes of both player and listener towards each other much more frequently than occasion demanded—smile answered smile, and tell-tale blushes hung out their signals of distress; in truth it was a repetition of the old, old story

> Which has been since the world began,
> And shall be till its close.

Bryan Maguire, despite his plighted vow of constancy to

Winnie Byrne—a vow wrung from him through the influence of an evil power—there and then, in the exuberance of a love as pure as it was exalted, declared his passion in a few simple phrases, and was honestly accepted. It was not until the fatal die was cast and cooler moments returned to him, that his conscience whispered of the serious consequences likely to ensue, but when he contrasted the fair and refined creature from whom he had reluctantly torn himself, with the coarse uncultured girl who tried to lure him like a syren, to his destruction, he felt satisfied that his honour was not imperilled. Day after day he framed some excuse for visiting at the Rectory. The clergyman was too deeply engrossed with his books and antiquities to suspect even dimly, the existence of the attachment; while on the other hand, the temporary absence of Winnie Byrne from home, left everything smooth for the course of their affection. And it was now that a new life seemed to dawn upon our hero; the scales had fallen from his eyes—his hitherto settled conviction that beauty, virtue, and refinement could not be found in the same being, was disproved; his path of love was strewn with flowers, and all that marred his happiness was the presence of her who was the first to make him feel the illusory pleasure of sensual or merely human affections.

Even while these and similar thoughts were struggling in his mind, the web of his destiny was being woven, and his destruction planned by the discarded Winnie and her accomplice, who acted the part of a spy over all his movements; and who, for some real or supposed wrong done to one of her family by an ancestor of Bryan's, determined to wreak vengeance on his head. Alas! for frail humanity, she found a fitting tool in Winnie Byrne for the accomplishment of her hellish plans; for it was through her advice that the young woman wrought the spells which so effectually over-reached him at the holy well.

It was a bright morning in August, and the sun was shining forth with all his splendour, bathing in golden light the hills and vales around Moate-Granoge. Farmer Maguire's reapers were preparing to commence the harvest, and many a pleasant jest went round as they munched the ripe apples that were distributed amongst them by the farmer's generous wife. But where was Winnie Byrne, whose wont it was to take the prize at binding the farmer's corn in former years? Verily she was not far off, for just then she was concealed behind a fence with Sinead the witch.

'Did I not tell you,' said the latter, 'that it was better to bide the hour of vengeance than to make a scene over the matter? You have only to follow my instructions to bring both death and destruction to him and *her*—the hardened heretic that took him from you, *alanna*. Just step into the cornfield as unconcerned as ever and tie the first sheaf, taking care to shape nine hearts out of nine ears, and stick a pin through each one of them. This will *do* for her within a year and a day if you bury it under nine feet of earth. For him put down a bottle of blood in a grave and stamp on it nine times. It will soon burst, and so will his heart at the same moment.'

The misguided girl, actuated by disappointed love and jealousy, faithfully obeyed the crone's instructions. There are powers of evil whose operations and functions we understand not, and therefore why should we endeavour to account for the fact—for fact it was—that within the year and the day Bryan Maguire and his new love were both gathered to their fathers. His death was rather tragical, occurring on the funeral day of his affianced bride. Nor did Winnie Byrne long survive; disappointed, remorseful, and broken-hearted, she actually withered away, manifesting a sad example of the result of ungoverned earthly affections and passions. Even to this day the deadly nightshade grows upon her unhallowed grave.

A TERRIBLE REVENGE

The Irish fairies often take a terrible revenge if they are ever slighted or offended. A whole family once came under their ban because a fairy woman had been refused admittance into the house. The eldest boy lost his sight for some time, and though he recovered the use of his eyes yet they always had a strange expression, as if he saw some terrible object in the distance that scared him. And at last the neighbours grew afraid of the family, for they brought ill-luck wherever they went, and nothing prospered that they touched.

There were six children, all wizened little creatures with withered old faces and thin crooked fingers. Every one knew they were fairy changelings, and the smith wanted to put them on the anvil, and the wise women said they should be passed through the fire; but destiny settled the future for them, for one after another they all pined away and died, and the ban of the fairies was never lifted from the ill-fated house till the whole family lay in the grave.

THE CLONMEL WITCH BURNING

JIM McGARRY

Ballyvadlea is a little village set among the pleasant farmlands of County Tipperary, not far from the town of Clonmel. Looking out over a rich valley in the Knockmealdon Mountains, it is peaceful and isolated. But in 1895 it was the scene of an event at once sinister and terrifying in its primitive brutality.

On Wednesday, March 20th, 1895, the following paragraph appeared in the *Clonmel Chronicle*, under the heading 'Gone with the Fairies'.

'A good deal of excitement has been caused in the district around Drangan and Cloneen by the mysterious disappearance of a farm labourer's wife, who lived with her husband in this part of the country. The poor woman had been ill for some time, and a few days ago she told her husband that if he did not do something for her by a certain time "she would have to be going". An old woman who was nursing her was sitting up with her one night last week when, as she puts it, the invalid was "drawn away". A search has been made everywhere and the police communicated with, but so far no trace of the missing woman has been found. The country people entertain the opinion that she has "gone with the fairies".'

Three days later, on March 23rd, the same paper carried a story that wild rumours were circulating about the woman's disappearance, which had now become a topic of intense interest in the area.

Exactly a week before these articles appeared, Dr Crean, a local physician, and Father Ryan, a priest from the district, in making their usual calls upon the sick, had visited a young woman called Bridget Cleary, wife of the cooper of Ballyvadlea. She was attractive, only twenty-six years old and not seriously ill. The doctor prescribed some medicine for a bronchial condition, the priest conversed with her; neither man had cause to feel particular concern on her behalf, and there was certainly

54

no hint of the terrible fate that was so soon to befall her. But between their visits and the first news of her disappearance in the newspaper, Bridget Cleary was to undergo torments of almost unbelievable horror.

On the day following the visits from the priest and the doctor, a Mr and Mrs Simpson, Mrs Johanna Burke and her ten-year-old daughter Katie, who were neighbours of Bridget and concerned at her illness, decided to go and see her. But they were unable to get into her house. They could hear voices from inside, however, and later reported hearing someone shouting, 'Take it you bitch, you old faggot, or we'll kill you.'

They had arrived at about seven o'clock in the evening and, after persistent efforts, were eventually admitted about an hour later, to witness a scene both horrible and extraordinary.

Gathered round the sick woman and holding her down on her bed, were four men: John Dunne, an elderly man who lived near by, and three brothers, James, Patrick and William Kennedy. Their mother, Mary, a sixteen-year-old boy called William Aherne and Bridget's father, Patrick Boland, stood by watching, while Michael Cleary forced a spoonful of herbal mixture down his wife's throat. The visitors were told that these herbs had come from a man named Ganey, of Kyleathlea, which was over the mountains. He was supposed to be an expert in witchcraft, and enjoyed a high reputation among the superstitious.

Having administered the mixture, Bridget's husband then called for another liquid to be brought. This turned out to be urine and he ordered it to be thrown over her. This was done not once but several times, the whole scene being lit by a candle held by William Aherne.

Bridget was struggling, and screaming, 'Let me alone,' and, afraid that her cries would attract the attention of a passer-by, one of the men put his hand over her mouth. The others then lifted her off the bed and started to swing her backwards and forwards across it, and as they swung her they shouted: 'Come home, Bridget Boland.'

The cries of the stricken woman, coupled with the men's fear that she was possessed by an evil spirit, seemed to drive them to an intense, albeit subconscious, sadism. Apparently unsatisfied with the results of their treatment so far, they proceeded to carry her, kicking and screaming, to the kitchen fire, where, on the advice of John Dunne, they laid her across the red-hot bars of the grate. Almost out of her mind with pain and terror, she was questioned three times by her husband and her father: 'Are you Bridget Boland, wife of Michael Cleary in the name of God?' and three times, in a broken voice, she answered that she was.

At this stage, the onlookers noticed that the wretched woman had great red weals across her forehead, and learned that these had been caused by a red-hot poker being laid across it as an inducement to take Ganey's medicine. The position of the Simpsons and Mrs Burke in all this seems to have been somewhat invidious. Whilst claiming that they were unable to leave the house owing to the fact that Michael Cleary had locked all the doors, they nevertheless watched Bridget Cleary being tortured until six o'clock the next morning and Mrs Burke, at any rate, did not hesitate to return the following evening, accompanied once again by her small daughter. Furthermore, at no time during Bridget Cleary's ordeal did any of them attempt to rescue her, though they may have been influenced in this by the fact that Johanna Burke was a sister of the Kennedy boys.

And so, on the evening of March 15th, Michael Cleary, Patrick Boland, John Dunne and the Kennedy brothers resumed their torture of Bridget, William Aherne once more acting as light bearer. Early on in the evening, Bridget made one pathetic attempt to stop her tormentors by crying out that the peelers, as the police were called, were at the window, but it had little effect. Her interrogation continued, much of it concerned with changelings and fairies, and at one point she turned to her husband and said: 'Your mother was going with the fairies, that's why you say I'm going now.' Michael then asked her if his mother had told her this, to which she replied, 'She did that, she gave two days with them.'

The night wore on, the proceedings having assumed a gruesome pattern of interrogation and torture. She was forced to swallow another liquid, described as holy water, and was then subjected to a ritual known as the ordeal by bread, where the victim was fed three pieces of bread and jam. She managed two pieces but failed to eat the third. At this point Mrs Burke cried out, 'Leave her alone, Mike. Don't you see it's Bridget that is in it?' but she knew that he suspected that Bridget was a fairy, and not his wife. And all the time, the tension in the little cottage was mounting, until the atmosphere of savagery and sadism had them all in its grip. Michael Cleary, in pursuit of some evil and undefined purpose, could not be stopped at this stage, and eventually, almost hysterical, he stripped his wife as she lay on the bed, and taking a blazing stick from the fire, held it over her. Slowly he brought it to her mouth, as he gabbled his savage, monotonous questions, and from time to time the burning wood singed her lips. Then he had her brought to the open fireplace, to be swung over the flames.

By now her screams were unrestrained and must surely have been heard by the neighbours, but they were cowed by the obvious presence of evil, and remained in their houses, unwilling to become involved. The horror by now had reached a climax. Dragging Bridget from the fire, her husband threw his blazing stump of wood at her, setting the last scraps of her clothing alight. But Michael was still unsatisfied, still seeking a terrible catharsis. He grabbed some oil that was kept for the lamps and flung it over her, to feed the flames on her burning body. The house became dark with smoke as she blazed on the hearth, and Michael turned to his silent audience and cried: 'It is not Bridget I am burning, you will soon see her flying up the chimney.'

It was soon over. In a few minutes Bridget Cleary's long agony was past, and she lay on the hearth, her limbs cramped, her back and the lower part of her body horribly burned, the internal organs protruding through her burned flesh. Her hands were burned, her tongue lacerated and discoloured, her neck injured by attempted strangulation. But her face had been comparatively untouched, and the people in the little room noticed that it still bore the quality of beauty.

Terror at what they had done was now borne in on everyone in the cottage. There was an awful silence, broken only by the whimpering of the child, Katie Burke. Even Michael Cleary was momentarily silenced, stilled by the hideous act he had just committed. But he was the first to recover, to understand the implications and to make arrangements for his own safety.

He pulled the sheets from Bridget's bed and wrapped the twisted body of his wife in them. He had to use a lot of persuasion, but eventually he prevailed upon Pat Kennedy to help him bury the body. At about two o'clock in the morning, they carried her out of the house, and a quarter of a mile away, in a waterlogged field, they dug a shallow grave. Into it they laid the naked, mutilated corpse. Someone had put some black stockings over the remains of Bridget's legs and Michael Cleary had found a sack to pull over her head. They then covered her with a thin layer of clay and some bushes to disguise the disturbed ground.

During the week that followed, the police started an intensive search for the missing woman, but her murder was not suspected at that time. Then, on Friday, March 22nd, her body was discovered by a Sergeant Rogers of Mullinahone, and the investigations began in earnest.

Questioned about the night of March 15th, Johanna Burke first alleged that when she arrived at the Clearys' house, she found Bridget on her way out, dressed only in a nightdress and apparently raving mad. She said she had tried to stop her, but to no avail, and though Bridget's husband had gone in search of her, he had been unsuccessful. Later, she gave a full statement to the police, including a description of Michael Cleary on the morning after the murder, scraping the leg of his trousers with a knife, and saying to her, 'Oh, God, Han, there is a substance of poor Bridget's body,' while he removed the grease stains.

William Simpson, who had witnessed Bridget's first night of torment, also gave a statement to the police, as a result of which the *Clonmel Chronicle* reported: 'Investigations by the police under District Inspector J. A. Wansborough of Carrick-on-Suir, and information sworn by William Simpson, caretaker, of Cloneen, and a woman named Burke, have resulted in warrants being issued for the arrest of nine persons. Eight were charged with being implicated severally and jointly in ill treatment of the woman. The ninth was charged with having caused the offence to be committed.'

The eight in question were Michael Cleary, Patrick Boland, John Dunne, Patrick, James and Michael Kennedy, their mother Mary, and William Aherne. The ninth, Dennis Ganey, was charged with having caused her ill treatment by his advice and instructions. All nine were remanded, and bail was refused. At the first hearing, and throughout all subsequent ones, an angry crowd, appalled by the crime, waited in the streets of Clonmel while the prisoners were being taken to the courthouse, and police protection of an elaborate sort was needed to prevent them falling into the hands of the mob.

James J. Shee, J.P., coroner for the district, held an inquest near the scene of the crime. He described it as being 'one of the most frightful things that has occurred in this county for years.' At his suggestion, and in the absence of the accused, the inquest confined its evidence to a medical report, the result of a post-mortem. The coroner's jury found that burns, inflicted by a person or persons unknown, had caused the death of poor, young, beautiful Bridget Cleary.

That night, by the light of a lamp, Bridget Cleary was buried in Cloneen churchyard. Such was the atmosphere of superstition and fear in the district that no man nor woman could be found to assist at her burial, and it was carried out by the police.

After several hearings before the Magistrates during which the accused sought, by various means, to explain away their participation in the events, they were all returned for trial to the Clonmel Assizes, which were held in July. The presiding judge, Judge O'Brien, said in his summing up: 'This case demonstrates a degree of darkness in the mind, not of one person but of several, a moral darkness, even a religious darkness, the disclosure of which has come as a shock to many people.'

The sentences were surprisingly lenient, following the withdrawal by the Crown Prosecutor of the charge of 'murder'. Michael Cleary was found guilty of manslaughter, and sentenced to twenty years penal servitude. Patrick Kennedy, who was found guilty of wounding, was sentenced to five years penal servitude. John Dunne was sent away for three years penal servitude and James and William got a year and a half's imprisonment. Michael Kennedy and Patrick Boland were sent to prison for six months, but Mary Kennedy was freed by the judge, with the emotive words, 'I will not pass any sentence on this poor old woman.' It was a sympathy and concern that had not been shown to the wretched victim of Ballyvadlea.

The case of the unhappy young woman, Bridget Cleary, has one distinction, albeit a terrible one. It was the last burning of a witch in the history of Western Europe.

THE HARTPOLE DOOM

There is a tradition concerning the Hartpole family of Shrule Castle in the Queen's County (called 'The Castle on the Bloody Stream', from the sanguinary deeds of the owner) that every male member of the family is doomed and fated to utter three screeches, terrible to hear, when dying. As to the origin of this doom, the story goes that Sir Richard Hartpole, about 300 years ago, in the time of the Elizabethan wars, committed many savage acts against the Irish, he being an upholder of the English faction.

One day a priest named O'More, came to the castle on some friendly mission. The savage Hartpole ordered his retainers to seize the priest and hang him up in the courtyard.

'Good God!' exclaimed the priest. 'Give me at least a moment to pray!'

'Go then,' said Hartpole, 'you may pray.'

The priest kneeled down apart from the crowd. But Hartpole grew impatient, and ordered him to rise.

'You have prayed long enough,' he said, 'prepare for death.'

And when the priest heard the order for his death, and saw the man approach to seize him, he swayed from right to left and gave three fearful screams.

'Why do you screech?' asked the tyrant.

'So shall you scream, and all your descendants in your last agony,' exclaimed O'More, 'as a sign of the doom upon your race. You have murdered my people, you are now going to take my life; but I lay the curse of God on you and yours. Your property shall pass away; your race shall perish off the earth; and by the three death screeches all men shall know that you and your posterity are accursed.

The words of O'More only made the tyrant more furious, and the priest was hung at once in the courtyard before the eyes of Hartpole. But the prophecy of doom was fulfilled. The property perished, the castle became a ruin. The last Hartpole died miserably of want and hunger, and the whole race finally has become extinct.

THE DIPLOMATIST'S STORY
SHANE LESLIE

The diplomatic race are expected to go through life telling excellent and wisely conceived falsehoods for the benefit of their country. In the art of elegant lying there is a call for proficiency whenever the world seeks to soften the display of its own powers of intrigue and corruption. It has been noticed that any country which breeds efficient horse-dealers can generally produce a good average diplomatist. This may possibly be a reason why so many Irishmen from North or South have excelled in the glittering paths which lead from the gates of the British Foreign Office.

During the reign of Victoria no Irishman excelled more deservedly in British diplomacy than the late Lord Monaghan, whose breeding was a pleasant mixture of the dour Ulsterman and the kindlier cunning of the South. Anglo-Irish writers and Dublin Court beauties figured in his pedigree. At an early age he had been inveigled into the Foreign Office by the promise of a career. Post had followed post over nearly half a century. At the end of it he had stepped into a Victorian peerage and retired to an ancient Irish demesne, which like many Irish demesnes was composed chiefly of Lough water and even more so in the rainy weather.

Lord Monaghan was socially much sought in the North of Ireland since his retirement. No garden-party or county function was considered complete without his appearance. He always wore a carefully prepared costume of the Third Empire based on the tailoring of the Emperor whom he had known and entertained in his later days of exile. This facial resemblance, of which he was a little proud on the Continent, was completed by a tiny tuft of hair under his lip. During each autumn he paid visits to the big houses of the North. There was only one castle which he seemed anxious to avoid. He refused invitations thereto, whether for the afternoon or for a prolonged stay. He always refused and would never give reasons. It was known that he had paid a visit there in his youth nearly half a century before but that he had never returned. The countryside decided that he must have been refused in marriage by a daughter of the house and had retained an acute memory of the sting. He himself would never say why, and there was a natural delicacy in questioning him in his own country.

Towards the end of his life an uncle of mine met him in the train travelling from Paris to the Riviera. It was in the days before the hordes of English who either had no income or else had to dodge an income tax, began pouring into the sunshine of the Mediterranean. Invalids and retired diplomatists chiefly composed the mixed company to be found grilling under the cloudless heat. Strangers in the train were generally found to be distinguished and worthy of conversation. Accidentally my uncle mentioned that he had been staying at Mullymore Castle. Then he remembered where Lord Monaghan never went and with some secret reason for his conduct. The old diplomatist never as much raised the hair of an eyebrow. But my uncle must have caught his thought, for a minute later he knew that he had been tactless and danced back over the conversational Tom Tiddler's ground. Feeling he had left some memory awake that had better been left to slumber he tried to turn conversation into another channel, but, as is often the way, his mental reservation, not to mention the name of Mullymore, led him to blurting it out again ten minutes later.

'What does Mullymore Castle look like to-day?' asked Lord Monaghan quickly, as though to release my uncle from the embarrassment into which he had fallen. My uncle described it much as he had seen it a month previously. Lord Monaghan, flitting back nearly half a century, listened quietly to his account, only observing at the end: 'It was much the same in the old days, but I don't remember the whitewash of which you speak.'

'Yes, it is whitewashed now like a peasant's cottage,' said my uncle, 'one of the English wives found it gloomy so they tried to cheer things up. And they have changed the entrance drive from the porch side into garden-beds.'

For the first time Lord Monaghan made a sign of interest. 'May I ask why they did that?' 'Same reason, I suppose.'

Both of them relapsed into dreamy silence bolstered by the cushions of a French express. It was the same picture of Irish landscape which both men were visioning behind their closing eyelids: a three-storied grey old castle with a windowless tower at the back, and a heavy porch on the west or windward side. Large sash-windows opened out of the walls. Whatever had been the ancient castellation it had given way to battered chimneys built of brick. But no repairs or additions could make it appear modern. It had a bare and bleak aspect and even after dark when it was illuminated by oil lamps within, it resembled a skull with lucifer matches burning behind the grey partitions of the bonework.

It was the same old building which both men visioned until the agreeable call came for lunch and they both moved down the corridor into the restaurant. Conversation broke out afresh. My uncle kept it to subjects which he thought must be agreeable as well as interesting to Lord Monaghan. It was the old diplomat who suddenly brought the talk back to Mullymore. They had been talking about the coincidences that were most difficult to explain in life but such as are bound to occur once or twice in everybody's experience. Lord Monaghan said that in his long career only once had the inexplicable crossed him, but with results which had reappeared during his life like an echo. It bordered on the supernatural and had convinced him that there could be occasions when four and four would fail to total eight. In other words there were times when the rules of mathematics did not apply to the logic of life.

'When I was a young man struggling between the University and the Foreign Office,' continued Lord Monaghan, 'I went to stay at Mullymore. It was a very long time ago. The old Dowager was still alive and her four daughters were in waiting upon her, and perhaps in waiting for husbands as well, though they did not seem to mind whether they ever got away from the old castle. It appeared to have laid a hand of possession on them all. People may claim that they own houses out of the past, but I have often known such houses entirely possess their inhabitants. Mullymore was one of them.

'I was entertained with old-world hospitality. The son of the family acted as my host. I was not worried to play games.

I was left entirely to myself, for which I was grateful. I recall it all as though it were yesterday. The old Dowager sitting there with her ear-trumpet clashing against her soiled old family jewellery. She directed me to the Porch room, a long, chilly chamber, which looked out upon the drive as it used to be. You say that it has been changed around, do you not? Well, hereby may hang a tale. Towards the end of my last afternoon we were all sitting in the drawing-room. The five ladies were delicately administering tea to the two men present when we all heard the sound of carriage wheels on the drive, but so clearly that it raised no doubt. There was a noise of solid gravel being crunched and the regular stroke of horses' hoofs. All came to a halt outside the porch.

'The old lady looked up and mentioned that she could not imagine who would want to be calling that day. Nobody was invited or expected. And if I remember correctly, she added that nobody was wanted. A few minutes passed without anybody appearing. She rang the bell for the major-domo and ordered him to show in whoever the visitors might be. He returned to say that there was none waiting in the porch and that the bell had never been rung from the outside. At this the old lady turned pale but maintained her courage. "This," she said, "is very sad for our family", before she relapsed into silence. You can guess from other and similar stories that you have heard that it was a manner of death-warning.

'But the supernatural aspect did not dawn on me until an hour later, though the warning by ghostly carriage-wheels is told of more than one Irish family. It is only the sequel which is interesting in this case. The old lady refused to be upset, sitting over her tea for an hour but still looking as white as her cap of white lace. The young ladies continued to make tea assiduously for the non-arriving guests and I myself carried on a faint conversation until the usual hour for retiring to our rooms, when the gong rang bidding us to dress for dinner. On our way upstairs my host observed to me that he had very distinctly heard the carriage wheels on the drive, and asked me my opinion. I answered that I had heard them no less. He then casually informed me that they had a family Banshee: that whenever a member of their family was about to die, however distantly related, a carriage was always rolling up the drive, although it was never seen.

'The legend went back several generations. The origin was simple enough. An ancestor had been killed returning home from Dublin when his high carriage crashed behind drunken postillions. In those days travellers were as much in the hands of their postillions as they are in the power of chauffeurs to-day. His wife had been expecting him all day and when she heard, as she believed, his wheels outside the porch she had run out eagerly to find nobody. The same day her husband had been killed the other side of Drogheda.'

Lord Monaghan recalled the deep impression this simple and not uncommon story of the supernatural had made upon him. But he had never learnt which member of the family had perished in answer to the particular warning he had heard. Some very distant cousin possibly, but he had not stayed to hear. That was his last night at Mullymore. What happened after dinner was as follows. He went to bed in the Porch room the same as on preceding nights, when he was awakened by the same chariot wheels on the gravel which had disturbed the house-party at the tea hour. He turned over to sleep but was roused by the same sound again. He sat up and realized that he was far from dreaming. The noise of horses on the gravel was as distinct as the ticking of his watch. He had the strength of nerve to find his way to the window and, as he might have expected, he caught sight of an old-fashioned coach poised on its high wheels. Uncertain whether it was an optical illusion caused by the glass or not, he opened the window. There could be little doubt of the reality presented to his visual senses, for the sound of voices reached him from below. He watched and saw two men carrying a shapeless mass from the porch into the carriage. He was caught in the fascination of the moment which seemed to be drawn out timelessly. It might have taken a few seconds and it might have occupied half an hour, but he kept his senses. When the black mass, which he vaguely recognized as a coffin, had been pushed on board the chariot, the two men climbed to the seats behind and gave the order to proceed

Then Lord Monaghan observed that there was a coachman

on the box who turned deliberately round and looking up caught him full in the eyes, and said in words never to be forgotten: *Il y a place encore pour un.* Every word was clearly enunciated in French, but why in French? Lord Monaghan thought that he must have been more receptive in that language at that time, for he had been working very hard for his examinations at the Foreign Office. All those days he was thinking and dreaming in French. This might account for any subconscious revelation reaching him in that language. But to the end of his life he believed he had been awake all the time. He distinctly remembered walking round and round the room long after the carriage had disappeared, rumbling away like any other carriage on its wheels. The next morning he had left Mullymore never to return.

Fifty years had passed since he had enjoyed as great a career as a man with good fortune and fair talents could expect. He had had all that the world could offer him. He had accepted the standards, the conventions, and the diplomacy of the world. Even the religion of the world he found matter of fact and accepted as part of the international structure it was his duty to preserve. But there was something running through his life, it was true with considerable gaps, which was not matter of fact. It was simply that those words which he had heard uttered in the porch room in that distant Irish castle had not exactly haunted him, but from time to time he had heard them re-uttered with no little import to his career. For intervals of years he entirely forgot the words. He might hear and use them himself without recalling anything strange in the past, but there were strange occasions when they sounded like an echo of destiny.

He would give a few instances. When he was a young Secretary at the Foreign Office, he was intensely anxious to be included in an Embassage which was being sent out at the time to the East. It was a joint expedition shared by the French and promised some months of novelty in the East as well as assuring a step to all who were its partakers. Feeling that his career might pivot from his inclusion he applied for even the lowest position. There were two Secretaries to be chosen to accompany the English-Plenipotentiaries. He relied on his record, his examinations and his hard work, but he had no string he could pull in his own favour. An anxious moment arrived when the Minister for Foreign Affairs himself decided who were to go. So anxious was he that he spent the morning pacing the passage outside the Minister's room in mingled dread and hope. He watched the French representatives arrive and depart. An Under-Secretary had promised to let him know as soon as the decision was made in the inner councils. Well, his friend had appeared and told him that the other two Secretaries had been chosen over his head, but that his claims had been highly considered. As he stifled his disappointment and walked down the corridor he met the French representative returning on his tracks to tell the Foreign Secretary that as the French were including a Commercial Secretary beyond their quota of two there was room for another Englishman. He heard him as he disappeared behind the door say to his friend the Under-Secretary: '*Mais il y a place encore pour un.*'

The moment he heard those syllables he felt no more doubt, anxiety or disappointment. The words seemed to ring in his ears like the bell of good luck. He felt no surprise the following day when he was asked officially to join the embassage, and from that moment in his career he had never looked back.

There were a dozen other times in his life when those same words had rung out and always by the necessity of circumstances in French. He had always been able to associate their occurrence with some startling event in his life: at least every time that the words affected him. There must have been many unimportant occasions when he had heard the phrase as a phrase during his many years spent in Paris, but these he did not remember.

But the strangest occasion of all had been in Paris and that he could never forget. He had gone out to pay a visit to some French friends living in the fifth story of an apartment house. It was a good many years back and the new system of American elevators had been recently introduced into European capitals. The liftman had taken him successfully up. It was almost a novel sensation in those days. After using this mechanical

means of ascent to the fifth floor Lord Monaghan paid his
intended visit and an hour later prepared to return to the
Embassy, where he was quartered. The lift was descending
from a higher floor. The lift appeared to be already full,
and though the gates were swung open he had hesitated to
enter. The people in the lift had shuffled a little, and the liftman
called out in the most natural voice: '*Il y a place encore pour
un!*' So quietly and naturally did the liftman pronounce his
words that they raised no immediate tremor of memory in
Lord Monaghan's mind. He already had one foot in the lift
and was raising himself on the other when he caught sight
of the liftman's face, and their eyes met full. Thoughts and
memories passed with colliding force in the space of a hun-
dredth of a second. It was a face he had seen before, and those
were eyes into which he had once looked with wondering fear,
but how long ago? And where? Was it an ancient dream? . . .
And there swam back into memory an old Irish castle with
a carriage drive running up to the porch. Thirty or forty years
were as yesterday, and he remembered the features of the
driver on the box of the phantom coach at Mullymore Castle.
His second foot was already in the air but not in the lift,
but he had the strength of mind subconsciously exerted to
hurl himself backwards and to remain on the landing while
the lift with quickly closing doors sped swiftly downward.
There was a broken brake and the lift crashed . . . Everybody
in the lift, including the liftman, was killed . . .

NOVEMBER EVE

All the spells worked on November Eve are performed in the name of the devil, who is then forced to reveal the future fate of the questioner. The most usual spell is to wash a garment in a running brook, then hang it on a thorn bush, and wait to see the apparition of the lover, who will come to turn it. But the tricks played on this night by young persons on each other have often most disastrous consequences. One young girl fell dead with fright when an apparition really came and turned the garment she had hung on the bush. And a lady narrates that on the first of November her servant rushed into the room and fainted on the floor. On recovering, she said that she had played a trick that night in the name of the devil before the looking-glass; but what she had seen she dared not speak of, though the remembrance of it would never leave her brain, and she knew the shock would kill her. They tried to laugh her out of her fears, but the next night she was found quite dead, with her features horribly contorted, lying on the floor before the looking-glass, which was shivered to pieces.

THE SORCERERS
W. B. YEATS

In Ireland we hear but little of the darker powers, and come across any who have seen them even more rarely, for the imagination of the people dwells rather upon the fantastic and capricious, and fantasy and caprice would lose the freedom which is their breath of life were they to unite them either with evil or with good. And yet the wise are of opinion that wherever man is, the dark powers, who feed his rapacities; no less than the bright beings, who store their honey in the cells of his heart; and the twilight beings who flit hither and thither; encompass him with their passionate and melancholy multitude. They hold, too, that he who by long desire or through accident of birth possesses the power of piercing into their hidden abode can see them there, those who were once men or women full of a terrible vehemence, and those who have never lived upon the earth, moving slowly and with a subtler malice. The dark powers cling about us, it is said, day and night, like bats upon an old tree; and that we do not hear more of them is merely because the darker kinds of magic have been but little practised. I have indeed come across very few persons in Ireland who try to communicate with evil powers, and the few I have met keep their purpose and practice wholly hidden from the inhabitants of the remote town where they live. It is even possible, though this is perhaps scarcely likely, that their lives will leave no record in the folklore of the district. They are mainly small clerks and the like, and meet for the purpose of their art in a room hung with black hangings. They would not admit me into this room, but finding me not altogether ignorant of the arcane science, showed gladly elsewhere what they would do. 'Come to us,' said their leader, a clerk in a large flour-mill, 'and we will show you spirits who will talk to you face to face, and in shapes as solid and heavy as our own.'

I had been talking of the power of communicating in states of trance with the angelical and faery beings—the children of the day and of the twilight,—and he had been contending that we should only believe in what we can see and feel when in our ordinary everyday state of mind. 'Yes,' I said, 'I will come to you,' or some such words; 'but I will not permit myself to become entranced, and will therefore know whether these shapes you talk of are any the more to be touched and felt by the ordinary senses than are those I talk of.' I was not denying the power of other beings to take upon themselves a clothing of mortal substance, but only that simple instructions such as he spoke of, seemed unlikely to do more than cast the mind into trance and thereby bring it into the presence of the powers of day, twilight, and darkness.

'But,' he said, 'we have seen them move the furniture hither and thither, and they go at our bidding, and help or harm people who know nothing of them.' I am not giving the exact words, but as accurately as I can the substance of our talk.

On the night arranged I turned up about eight, and found the leader sitting alone in almost total darkness in a small back room. He was dressed in a black gown, like an inquisitor's dress in an old drawing, that left nothing of him visible except his eyes, which peered out through two small round holes. Upon the table in front of him was a brass dish of burning herbs, a large bowl, a skull covered with painted symbols, two crossed daggers, and certain implements shaped like quern stones, which were used to control the elemental powers in some fashion I did not discover. I also put on a black gown, and remember that it did not fit perfectly, and that it impeded my movements considerably. The sorcerer then took a black cock out of a basket, and cut its throat with one of the daggers, letting the blood fall into the large bowl. He then opened a book and began an invocation, which was certainly not English, and had a deep guttural sound. Before he had finished, another of the sorcerers, a man of about twenty-five, came in, and having put on a black gown also, seated himself at my left hand. I had the invoker directly in front of me, and soon began to find his eyes, which glittered through the small holes in his hood, affecting me in a curious way. I struggled hard against their influence, and my head began to ache. The invocation continued, and nothing happened for the first few minutes. Then the invoker got up and extinguished the light in the hall, so that no glimmer might come through the slit under the door. There was now no light except from the herbs on the brass dish, and no sound except from the deep guttural murmur of the invocation.

Presently the man at my left swayed himself about, and cried out, 'O god! O god!' I asked him what ailed him, but he did not know he had spoken. A moment after he said he could see a great serpent moving about the room, and became considerably excited. I saw nothing with any definite shape, but thought that black clouds were forming about me. I felt I must fall into a trance if I did not struggle against it, and that the influence which was causing this trance was out of harmony with itself, in other words, evil. After a struggle I got rid of the black clouds, and was able to observe with my ordinary senses again. The two sorcerers now began to see black and white columns moving about the room, and finally a man in a monk's habit, and they became greatly puzzled because I did not see these things also, for to them they were as solid as the table before them. The invoker appeared to be gradually increasing in power, and I began to feel as if a tide of darkness was pouring from him and concentrating itself about me; and now too I noticed that the man on my left hand had passed into a death-like trance. With a last great effort I drove off the black clouds, but feeling them to be the only shapes I should see without passing into a trance, and having no great love for them, I asked for lights, and after the needful exorcism returned to the ordinary world.

I said to the more powerful of the two sorcerers—'What would happen if one of your spirits had overpowered me?' 'You would go out of this room,' he answered, 'with his character added to your own.' I asked about the origin of his sorcery, but got little of importance, except that he had learned it from his father. He would not tell me more, for he had, it appeared, taken a vow of secrecy.

For some days I could not get over the feeling of having

a number of deformed and grotesque figures lingering about me. The Bright Powers are always beautiful and desirable, and the Dim Powers are now beautiful, now quaintly grotesque, but the Dark Powers express their unbalanced natures in shapes of ugliness and horror.

SLIABH-MISH, COUNTY KERRY

Everyone knows that Sliabh-Mish, County Kerry, is haunted. The figure of a man, accompanied by a huge black dog, is frequently seen standing on a high crag, but as the traveller approaches, the forms disappear, although they rise up again before him on another crag and so continue appearing and disappearing as he journeys on. Many travellers have seen them, but no one has ever yet been able to meet the man and the dog face to face on the mountain side, for they seem to melt away in the mist, and are seen no more on reaching the spot.

It happened, once upon a time, that a man, journeying alone over the mountain path, took out his snuff-box to solace himself with a pinch and was putting it up again in his waistcoat pocket, when he heard a voice near him saying, 'Not yet! Not yet! I am near you, wait.'

He looked round, but not a soul was to be seen. However, he thought it right to be friendly, so he shook some snuff from the box in the palm of his hand and held it out in the air. But his hair stood on end and he trembled with fright, when he felt invisible fingers on his hand picking up the snuff, and when he drew it back the snuff had disappeared.

'God and the saints between us and harm!' exclaimed the poor man, ready to drop down from terror.

'Amen,' responded the clear voice of some invisible speaker close beside him.

Then the man quickly made the sign of the cross over the hand touched by the spirit, and so went on his way unharmed.

THE HEADLESS RIDER OF
CASTLE SHEELA, COUNTY LIMERICK
JAMES REYNOLDS

Colour is a magic quality in this world. Colour takes many forms. There is the colour spectrum. There is the aura of colour surrounding a given person or place. The name of a family is often synonymous with colourful and exciting happenings in a house or locality. This is very true in the case of the 'Marvellous Mallorys' of Castle Sheela. The Family of Mallory, once Mael-ora, is large. Its ramifications are formidable and far flung. The term 'marvellous' is in effect a title. It might almost have been conferred by some monarch of a realm. Instead it is bestowed by all sorts of people, mostly with awe, now and again with jealousy, even with hate, as this story will bear out.

The village of Galtymore is near the demesne gates of Castle Sheela. The post intended for the Mallorys is sorted and dropped into 'the Castle bag' by old Mrs Carmody, the postmistress. It is she who best applies the word 'marvellous' to the Mallorys. One day, holding at arm's length a rose-coloured, crested envelope, covered with foreign stamps, postmarks, and forwarding addresses, the captivated Mrs Carmody said, 'Great marvels happen in the lives of all those Mallorys. Half the time they're walkin' the world, and the rest of the time they receive letters from it.' Hitching her square-cut spectacles a shade higher, she continued, 'They get letters from kings and potentates. In me mother's day, old Lady Mallory'd a letter from the Pope in Rome!'

Mrs Carmody seems to have capped the issue squarely. Marvels follow some people, to colour their lives, as ill-luck trails the less fortunate.

To Mrs Carmody I am enormously indebted in more ways than I can name. During my gathering of notes for this story, she answered a thousand questions, answered them with authority and great good humour, a wide smile or a tch-tch-tch, as

77

she thought proper to the mood. Her wit is expansive, crisp, and boundless. Colour and graciousness enfold this Irish country-woman, the like of a richly embroidered cloak.

With the early Mallorys we are not concerned in this narrative. The family flourished early on, in Irish history, and stems from antiquity. As an old man of the roads once told me when I asked him where a certain family had come from, 'Arragh, yer honour, nobody rightly knows the time. They rose out of a pile of stones, back and beyond in Fermanagh.' The first Gaelic Castle was a low, square pile of stones. The County Fermanagh is the antique cradle of many Gaelic families. With the exception of Turlough Mael-ora, who fought the Danes at the Battle of Clontarf in 1100, there is no early hero. The Mallorys have shone mostly under two crowns, which they adjusted on their handsome heads at will—sports and society.

In 1722, Brendan Mallory built a huge square house in the shadow of a half-ruined tower which had been built originally by Turlough Mael-ora to quarter his men and horses during the Battle of Clontarf. Later it was made habitable, and various members of the family lived there. One was an Abbott; Brother Constantine he called himself. This Mallory Abbott was a man of great piety, and it is said he founded an order of monks who lived in the tower for years. After he died and the present Castle Sheela was built, his forbidding presence was still felt. The gaunt, ivy-hung tower points a finger skyward and a shadow across the façade of Castle Sheela, as if to remind the gay, heedless, riotously living Mallorys that frivolity has no lasting substance, is but a pitfall for the soul. It is as if the old abbott continuously reminds his relatives that a seat in the Kingdom of Heaven awaits them, but only by the skin of their teeth will they make it.

In the vicinity of Galtymore—indeed, as far afield as Waterford, Cork and Dublin—if one so much as mentions the name of Mallory, some listener is bound to look up and ask sharply, 'The Mallorys? Which one? What have they done now?'

The family reached its peak of brilliant showmanship during the century between 1740 and 1850. During that period two of the male Mallorys contracted marriages with European women. These alliances brought Latin and Tartar-Hungarian blood into the family, thereby adding a veritable rainbow of colour to the already dazzling colour chart of the Irish Mallorys.

In 1739, Galty Mallory, the eldest son and heir to Castle Sheela, made the Grand Tour on the Continent. At that time Budapest was, to most European travellers, like a city on another planet. Travel over tortuous, brigand-infested mountain passes was a thing only the most daring and hardy man would attempt. The heavy spring and autumn rains in that part of the continent made long coach journeys unthinkable for three-fourths of the year. Budapest, therefore, sat in red, gold, and white barbaric splendour on the banks of the swiftly flowing Danube, brushing herself free from Turkish occupation, which she had endured for many years, without losing a sliver of her unique quality. Spread out behind Budapest, the like of a fabulously long train, billowed the Puszta, a vast, mirage-haunted plain.

Galty Mallory decided he wanted to visit this storied city of the Magyars. No roads of this world held any fears for Galty, so one spring day he set out from Vienna for Budapest, travelling by coach and later on horseback. For a part of the way the mud was nearly impassable. Then, as he came out of the Carpathian passes, down into the flat stretches of the Hungarian plain, oceans of spring greenness assailed him. He crossed the Puszta through acres and acres of wild flowers and waving spring wheat. Sitting astride his tired horse outside Budapest, Galty knew instantly that all the hardships of the long journey behind him had been worth it. Seen even from afar Budapest beckoned him with a magic peculiarly her own.

In Budapest all was splendour, Galty hastened to present a letter of introduction to a great friend of his father, Count Baylor Batoik-Illy. Count Baylor immediately set about arranging entertainments for the young Irish gentleman with the wide, engaging smile and a magnificent appreciation of fine horseflesh. Count Baylor bred the Hator-Orloff strain, beautiful and swift as any horse on earth.

Count Baylor had also bred an extremely beautiful daughter. His daughter and a stallion named Dragoro were the two living things he loved most. In the vaulted banquet hall at Castle Tata-Debrecen hung two huge portraits. One was a life-size painting of Dragoro, black as night. The other was of a tall, slim girl descending the green turf steps of a terrace. Behind her spread an arc of tall ash trees whose massive grey trunks gave great power to the composition of the picture. The girl seemed a dryad emerging from the forest, but a curious dryad, with high cheekbones and slanting, almost Chinese, eyes. There was a look of not-too-well-controlled wildness about the mouth of this arresting face. The mother of Countess Hoja Batoik-Illy was the daughter of a Tartar noble. There was more than a little of the furiously racing Tartar blood in Countess Hoja's veins.

Galty Mallory married Countess Hoja. After a year of travel, they returned to Ireland and settled, if one could ever consider the restless like of Countess Hoja 'settled', at Castle Sheela. In any case, she made Galty Mallory a supremely happy man, for he understood and played up to the constant wild adventures which were the breath of life to Countess Hoja Batoik-Illy Mallory, as she called herself. She bore Galty five children, two daughters and three sons. She was the mother of Ormond Mallory, wild as a hawk and handsome as Lucifer, whom in many other qualities he resembled—pride, for one. It is Ormond Mallory whose ghost now rides the staircase at Castle Sheela on Christmas night, a horseman without a head.

When Ormond Mallory's father died, the boy was eighteen years old. It was a madly dangerous age for a boy with the confused nature of Ormond to have so vast a sum of money at his command. Galty had, as he thought, very wisely provided for just this contingency. He had had no illusions about the waywardness, the arrogant pride of self, and the fiendish temper of the boy. All that was unstable and dross in the Mallory strain, coupled with the tempestuousness of his Tartar forbears, seemed to mingle in the bloodstream of Ormond Mallory. Immediately Galty was buried, Countess

Hoja had called Ormond into her sitting-room. She told him that, as the estate was entailed, it must go to him when he reached the age of twenty-one. What she proposed to do now was this: turn over to him at once the actual money that was to come to him. She and the three younger children would go for a long visit to her home in Debrecen. After placing the girls in a convent near Paris, she would return and take up residence at Knockrally, an old Charles II house belonging to the Mallorys at the harbour mouth of Waterford-Old City.

Ormond listened dutifully, albeit nervously, with one eye looking out the window at some of his hounds who were being taught the sport of coursing. His mother's absence would not cause him the slightest sorrow, for nothing in this world mattered to Ormond but Ormond.

As her son turned to leave the room, his mother said, rather bitterly, 'The reason for my making this change is this, much as I hate to admit it. The life you are set to lead frightens me. I do not wish to be a party to it. If I felt that I could do anything to stop it, I would try at least. I know I cannot. I have the girls to think of. If they lived in this house, no matter how closely chaperoned by me, they would be tarred by your brush. That is not a pretty picture. I will be blamed by many, I know, for deserting you at your age. But as you are already causing scandal in the village by forcing your attentions on young village girls, I see the way you wish to live, even while I am here. Your father is spared this, at least. It may be partly my fault. Your blood is dark with many crimes from my side of the family. Beware, Ormond, of the village men. However highly placed you may be, they will take their revenge.'

Ormond flicked a burr from his leather legging, bowed to his mother, and left the room. Countess Hoja thought to herself she might have spared her breath. Ormond had apparently not heard a word she had said.

Soon after this one-sided interview between Ormond and his mother, during which Ormond had said not one word, Countess Hoja and her two daughters set out for Hungary. Before she left, her second son, Dominic, was placed in a Franciscan school at Lisdoonvarna. Dominic was fifteen years old. He was not nearly so outrageously selfish as his brother Ormond, yet he was rebellious against authority. It was hoped the Franciscans would have a quieting influence. The third boy, last of the Mallory children, died when a small child.

From the moment that Ormond Mallory had Castle Sheela to himself, monarch of all he surveyed, his affairs took a lively turn. For more than a year, he had indulged himself with a rollicking widow who lived in the busy market town of Kilmallock. When Ormond had first met Moira Campbell, she was not a widow, but the predatory young wife of old John Carmichael, a prosperous chemist. When Carmichael died suddenly and was hurriedly buried, a few months after Moira's meeting with the handsome squire of Castle Sheela, ugly rumours flew like October leaves in and out of the doorways of Kilmallock. Moira, behind closed shutters, took stock of her chances. They did not look too bright if she remained in Kilmallock. She sold the chemist's shop and her small house with all her belongings. One month after the death of old John, Moira arrived at the portals of Ormond Mallory's house. She was accompanied by many boxes packed to bursting with new dresses and bonnets provided by the infatuated and generous Ormond.

Moira's arrival was quite open. The old transparent dodge of 'housekeeper', so often used by the gentry was spurned by both Moira and the defiant Ormond. She came as his mistress. She might, if her cards told true, end up as his wife.

For a few years we find Ormond occupied mostly with his horses and coursing greyhounds. His knowledge of horses was supreme. As the years passed, he became a power in racing and thoroughbred horse-breeding circles throughout Ireland. However badly Ormond Mallory was regarded by his more conventional neighbours for his loose way of living, men respected him as a fine sportsman. Women secretly envied Mistress Moira, but would have died before admitting it.

Moira Carmichael was a shocking housekeeper. The beautifully chosen furniture, which gave such an air of elegance and comfort to Castle Sheela, was in a sad state of disrepair in no time after her advent. The rooms which had been the talk of the countryside in Brendan Mallory's day were now a shambles. Packs of burr-matted dogs trooped through the suite of drawing-rooms on the first floor. Saddles, spurs, riding-crops, saddle-soap, coursing muzzles, and greasy horse bandages littered every chair and spilled over on to the floor. Fireplaces were never cleaned by the slack servants. Ashes lay in drifts on the floor and were ground into the pale amber rugs by booted feet. Whenever a door or window was opened, clouds of dust swirled through the house. If ever neglect rode wild, it was through the rooms of Castle Sheela.

Cheap, bawdy servants were all that Moira could manage. The decent Irish servitor would not set foot inside the house.

It is told in the village of Galtymore that Countess Hoja, on her return from Hungary, stayed for a while with friends near Castle Sheela. One day she rode over to pay her son a call. The front door standing open, she walked in. Frozen with amazement and anger at what she saw, the countess started forward to pull the bell cord. Deciding on another course, she walked through the rooms. Cobwebs hung in hammocks from picture frame to candelabrum and swayed back and forth in the breeze from the open door. A thick film of blue-grey dust lay on table tops and mantel shelves. Countess Hoja sailed furiously from room to room, her anger rising at every step. As she came out into the entrance hall, she saw a blowsy, heavy-eyed woman coming slowly down the stairs. It was Moira, newly awakened from sleep. Without a word the Countess Hoja approached the yawning woman and, raising her riding-crop, she dealt Moira a slashing blow across the face. Turning, she walked out of the house.

In the Mallory stables was a young hunter which Ormond called Follow, for the simple reason that even as a foal he would follow Ormond about the demesne very much as a dog will follow the one person he picks out on whom to centre a lifetime of affection and loyalty. Ormond fostered this trick, as he chose to regard it. He showed off Follow to his friends. One day, when Follow was a yearling, Ormond encouraged him to walk up the shallow stone steps leading to the entrance door of the castle. Ormond stood at the top and opened the door. When the young horse had successfully negotiated the steps, he walked through the door and without hesitation picked his way delicately up the rise of stairs to the door of Ormond's bedroom. This clever trick amused Ormond mightily. Next day he had a runway or ramp built at one side of the stairs. It was built in four broad, shallow rises and enabled Follow to mount the stairs and go down again with ease. At all hours of the day the horse would seek his master in this way. If Ormond was not in his room, Follow would return to the paddock. It came to be such a common sight to see the sleek sorrel horse marching up or down the ramp in the hall of Castle Sheela that no one even noticed. Certainly no one minded.

When Follow was four years old, Ormond started to hunt him with the Limerick Hounds. The horse was a superb mover, took his walls and ditches in a knowledgeable manner, and had a great heart. He endeared himself to the cold, sarcastic Ormond as no human had ever done. It finally got to the point that when Ormond was hunting and the meet was early in the morning, a groom would saddle Follow and the horse would walk out of the stable yard straight to the open front door of the house and march serenely up the ramp to his master's room. Then a little ceremony took place. Ormond would hold an apple in the palm of one hand and stick of sugar in the other. Follow would look first at one delicacy, then the other. Undecided for a moment, he would finally choose. Ormond would then spring into the saddle, and they were off to the meet. For two or three years this was a regular procedure. Moira had raged at the noise made by Follow's hoofs, of an early morning, on the wooden planking of the ramp. But Moira was gone from Castle Sheela. In the midst of one of her drunken rages, Ormond had packed her off. The last he had heard, she was living with a senile protector in Dublin.

For weeks there had been no one at Castle Sheela save Ormond, the ramping pack of greyhounds and terriers, and the constant visitor, Follow. In Ormond's tireless search for female companionship he roamed the countryside, playing the field. Playing the field spelled danger, the way Ormond did it. Flagrant and ruthless always, his complete disregard for another's feeling was his ultimate undoing.

Among the numerous women to whom Ormond paid marked attention was the boldly handsome but indiscreet wife of a neighbouring landowner, a man so devious in his dealings and of so jealous a nature that at times his actions smacked of madness. One day this man encountered his wife walking with Ormond Mallory in a secluded lane near the gates of Castle Sheela. What took place in this lane is not fully known. Ormond, however, was laid up for months with a broken shoulder.

During these days of enforced idleness, Follow visited Ormond every day. He had another visitor as well—a surprise visitor. His mother, hearing that Moira Carmichael was no longer at the Castle, rode over from Knockrally to stop the night. Ormond was secretly glad to see her, and was charm itself. He even consented to sit for his portrait, which his mother had long wanted him to have done, to hang in the dining-room at Castle Sheela along with portraits of his father and grandfather. An Italian painter named Cannorelli was living in Dublin. Ormond would ask him to pass the tedium of his inactivity. Besides sitting for his portrait, he could brush up on his Italian.

The other request his mother made was that he give a big Christmas party at Castle Sheela, a family party. He must ask his sisters, who had returned from their convent in France and were staying with their mother at Knockrally. Dominic, the brother, could come over for the party from Lisdoonvarna. Ormond told his mother to make whatever arrangements she desired. Countess Hoja returned to Knockrally considering her visit to her son a most successful one.

The portrait of Ormond Mallory was painted and hung 'on the line' in the dining-room beside his progenitors. It had a certain dash and fluid grace the other portraits lacked. The picture shows a slender man in his early thirties with a rather highly coloured face, little marred by dissipation. The hair is a light golden brown, unpowdered and tied at the nape of the neck by a wide black ribbon. He wears a dark green coat with silver buttons, and a black stock is loosely tied under the arrogant chin. The eyes arrest you. Cold, insolent, they are the hard steely blue of a winter evening sky. It is an inscrutable face. No one living could ever fathom what Ormond Mallory was thinking. The decoration of the portrait is given great style by a touch of the bizarre. As a compliment to his Hungarian mother, Ormond had flung over his shoulder a Csikós coat of white wool, heavily braided and embroidered in green, brown, and black.

The Christmas holiday season approached. Castle Sheela was put as much in order as was possible considering the shattered appearance left over from Moira Carmichael's sojourn. The Countess Hoja arrived accompanied by her daughters, Brigid and Caro. When Dominic arrived the afternoon of Christmas Eve, the family party at Castle Sheela was complete.

Late in the evening the Mallorys were sitting before the drawing-room fire. Goblets of light mulled wine were being passed around. Suddenly there was a sound of hoof-beats approaching rapidly along the hard, frosty driveway leading from the entrance gates to the Castle. The horse was pulled up sharply and the sound of an angry voice was heard at the front door demanding of a footman to speak to Ormond Mallory, 'Or by the holy God he'll wish he'd never been born!' Apparently Ormond recognized the shouting voice, for, as he hastily rose from his chair by the fire, his mother saw such a look of livid, intense hatred cloud his eyes that it frightened her. 'Ormond, what is it? Do you know who that is?' But Ormond had flung out of the room. She heard the front door slam with a force fit to wrench it off its hinges. No more was seen of Ormond that night.

Christmas morning dawned cold and overcast. Follow was the first one up at Castle Sheela. Long before the front door was opened by a sleepy maid, Follow was nuzzling the door-knob, wanting to be let in.

The meet for the Christmas Day hunt was to be held at Rillantora Park, an old abbey but recently made into a habitable house by Sir John Ainsley, an absentee landlord who had just inherited the place. The house had a dank, broody look even on a bright day. As the straggling riders cantered up to the abbey porch, assembling for the meet, many people shivered in their saddles, almost as much from dread of the house as from the biting wind. Through the densely packed trees of the park, the winter wind soughed and snapped off brittle branches. Horses champed at cold bits, riders banged gloved palms together to restore circulation, red noses ran unheeded. An unease was abroad. Old Lady Clonboy, atop a big raking grey, remarked to a man astride the horse next her, 'How Sir John can live in this old shebang is the wonder of the world. The drains are clogged with so much trash left over from the dark ages that it defies moving. More murders have been committed in this house than there are chimneys in the roof.'

At that moment a late horseman was seen approaching along a narrow ride cut through the trees in the park. It was Ormond Mallory, mounted on Follow. Ormond waved his crop, encompassing the entire group with one greeting. Some waved in return. The hunt moved off. But anyone looking closely at Ormond would have seen that he looked like death. His face was pale and drawn. His eyes shifted to right and left, nervously. His upper lip was puffy and there was a jagged cut at one corner of his mouth.

Christmas Day at Castle Sheela was far from a merry one. All day long there was a tension in the air that affected all within the house. Countess Hoja's neuralgia assailed her, so she kept to her room. Caro and Brigid tried embroidery. No use. Late in the morning they took the terriers for a walk through the old rabbit warrens at the back of the paddock. This kept the girls busy until they returned to join Dominic for a late lunch. Dominic had spent the morning browsing among his father's books in the library. 'Too cold to hunt,' he said.

In Terrance and Brendan Mallory's day, Christmas dinner at Castle Sheela had been a meal in the great tradition. On this particular Christmas, dinner was set for six o'clock in the evening, with Ormond Mallory presiding at the head of his table.

The day dragged on. Six o'clock came, but no Ormond appeared. Everyone knew the hunt had found its last fox around four o'clock. Dominic had walked out to the gate-house and talked with the huntsmen returning to Clonboy Castle. They told Dominic they had had a good day.

Mary Corty, the cook, was frantic. Dinner had been ready and waiting to be served these two hours. 'It'll be a great ruin, and meself destroyed with the labour,' she moaned. Then Kirstey, the maid who had opened the door early that morning for Follow, heard a noise on the stone steps of the entrance porch. It sounded like a heavy body stumbling. Then came the whinnying of a horse, a sobbing kind of whinnying, that of a horse far spent in wind. Kirstey ran to the door and flung it wide open. At the same moment Dominic appeared in the door of the library.

A foundering horse stumbled across the threshold of the hall door. His russet hide was streaked and matted with dried blood and lather.

Astride his back rode horror, the very definition of horror—the body of a man, the legs tied with a rope under the horse's belly, the wrists tied together behind the back. The dark green coat with silver buttons was torn and saturated with blood. Above the collar of this coat there was no head. Ormond Mallory's head had been severed cleanly from his body.

Too stunned by the shock of what they saw to move, Kirstey and Dominic sank back against the wall. Follow, his sides heaving in his last effort, slowly mounted the runway, as he had done daily for years. At the door of his master's bedroom he sank to the floor, dead.

The head of Ormond Mallory was never found, nor was his murderer ever discovered. Jason Fermoy, the neighbouring landowner who had met Ormond in the lane and beaten him with a shillelagh, as Jason later told at the Assizes Court, fell under suspicion and was interrogated by Mr Justice Callahan. Jason proved, beyond doubt, a watertight alibi. He was dismissed. A curious annotation on the margin of this phase of the case, is that, for years after the murder, Mrs Fermoy, heavily veiled, visited the grave of Ormond Mallory in the churchyard at Clonboy. After one of her visits a piece of paper, which she had tucked into a metal flower vase, was disturbed by an errant wind. The paper blew along one of the cemetery paths and was picked up by a lay priest who happened to be passing. Written in heavy black ink on a piece of stiff white paper was this:

EPITAPH
HE WAS WICKED, DESPERATELY WICKED.
BUT HE INVESTED WICKEDNESS
WITH A BRIGHTNESS AND SPARKLE
WHICH MADE IT EXCEEDINGLY ATTRACTIVE.

Soon after his brother Ormond's death, Dominic Mallory went to Italy. There, in Venice, he married a Signorina Lydia Canaletto, niece of the painter whose luminous pictures of the seventeenth-century Venice are world-famous. By this marriage Latin blood was infused into the Mallory strain. Countess Hoja died at Knockrally, and the Mallory girls both married Irishmen. It is Caro's great-great-great granddaughter, Mrs Torrance, who now lives at Castle Sheela.

When Dominic brought his Italian bride to Castle Sheela to live, the first thing he did was to remove the wooden ramp constructed by Ormond Mallory to accommodate his equine friend, Follow. But the mere absence of planking does not stop Follow from visiting his master's room as he always did when he was alive. Sometimes, just before dawn, the sound of hoofs hurrying rapidly up a phantom ramp is heard by persons in the house. If they listen they will hear (more sedately now, for the horse bears his master on his back) the iron-shod hoofs going down the ramp. Always on Christmas Day, after darkness has fallen, the front door will open suddenly and slam back against the wall.

Many people say they have seen a ghostly horse and rider mount the shadows beside the stair treads where the ramp used to be. The horse stumbles, as if nearly spent. The swaying rider has no head. Towards sunset on Christmas Day and on Christmas Day only, anyone looking at the portrait of Ormond Mallory, which now hangs over the fireplace in the dining-room, will be rather astonished. A change takes place. The arrogant face with the supercilious mouth is no longer there. Above the black satin stock there is only a dim smudge, which seems to glow with lambent fire. Next morning the painted face is again there, the blue, wintry eyes inscrutable.

A WOMAN'S CURSE

There was a woman of the Island of Innis-Sark who was determined to take revenge on a man because he called her by an evil name. So she went to the Saints' Well and, kneeling down, she took some of the water and poured it on the ground in the name of the devil, saying, 'So may my enemy be poured out like water, and lie helpless on the earth!' Then she went round the well backwards on her knees, and at each station she cast a stone in the name of the devil and said, 'So may the curse fall on him, and the power of the devil crush him!' After this she returned home.

Now the next morning there was a stiff breeze, and some of the men were afraid to go out fishing; but others said they would try their luck, and amongst them was the man on whom the curse rested. But they had not gone far from land when the boat was capsized by a heavy squall. The fishermen, however, saved themselves by swimming to shore; all except the man on whom the curse rested, and he sank like lead to the bottom, and the waves covered him, and he was drowned.

When the woman heard of the fate that had befallen her enemy, she ran to the beach and clapped her hands with joy. And as she stood there laughing with strange and horrid mirth, the corpse of the man she had cursed slowly rose up from the sea and came drifting towards her till it lay almost at her very feet. On this she stooped down to feast her eyes on the sight of the dead man, when suddenly a storm of wind screamed past her and hurled her from the point of rock where she stood. And when the people ran in all haste to help, no trace of her body could be seen. The woman and the corpse of the man she had cursed disappeared together under the waves and were never seen again from that time forth.

THE DREAM
JOSEPH SHERIDAN LE FANU

Dreams! What age, or what country of the world, has not felt and acknowledged the mystery of their origin and end? I have thought not a little upon the subject, seeing it is one which has been often forced upon my attentions, and sometimes strangely enough; and yet I have never arrived at anything which at all appeared a satisfactory conclusion. It does appear that a mental phenomenon so extraordinary cannot be wholly without its use. We know, indeed, that in the olden times it has been made the organ of communication between the Deity and His creatures; and when a dream produces upon a mind, to all appearance hopelessly reprobate and depraved, an effect so powerful and so lasting as to break down the inveterate habits, and to reform the life of an abandoned sinner, we see in the result, in the reformation of morals which appeared incorrigible, in the reclamation of a human soul which seemed to be irretrievably lost, something more than could be produced by a mere chimera of the slumbering fancy, something more than could arise from the capricious images of a terrified imagination. And while Reason rejects as absurd the superstition which will read a prophecy in every dream, she may, without violence to herself, recognize, even in the wildest and most incongruous of the wanderings of a slumbering intellect, the evidences and the fragments of a language which may be spoken, which *has* been spoken, to terrify, to warn and to command. We have reason to believe, too, by the promptness of action which in the age of the prophets followed all intimations of this kind, and by the strength of conviction and strange permanence of the effects resulting from certain dreams in latter times—which effects we ourselves may have witnessed—that when this medium of communications has been employed by the Deity, the evidences of His presence have been unequivocal. My thoughts were directed to this subject in a manner to leave a lasting impression upon my mind, by the events which I shall now relate, the statement of which, however extraordinary, is nevertheless accurate.

About the year 17—, having been appointed to the living of C——h, I rented a small house in the town which bears the same name: one morning in the month of November, I was awakened before my usual time by my servant, who bustled into my bedroom for the purpose of announcing a sick call. As the Catholic Church holds her last rites to be totally indispensable to the safety of the departing sinner, no conscientious clergyman can afford a moment's unnecessary delay, and in little more than five minutes I stood ready, cloaked and booted for the road, in the small front parlour in which the messenger who was to act as guide, awaited my coming. I found a poor little girl crying piteously near the door, and after some slight difficulty I ascertained that her father was either dead or just dying.

'And what may be your father's name, my poor child?' said I. She held down her head as if ashamed. I repeated the question, and the wretched little creature burst into floods of tears still more bitter than she had shed before. At length, almost angered by conduct which appeared to me so unreasonable, I began to lose patience, and I said rather harshly:

'If you will not tell me the name of the person to whom you would lead me, your silence can arise from no good motive, and I might be justified in refusing to go with you at all.'

'Oh, don't say that—don't say that!' cried she. 'Oh, sir, it was that I was afeard of when I would not tell you—I was afeard, when you heard his name, you would not come with me; but it is no use hidin' it now—it's Pat Connell, the carpenter, your honour.'

She looked in my face with the most earnest anxiety, as if her very existence depended upon what she should read there. I relieved the child at once. The name, indeed, was most unpleasantly familiar to me; but, however fruitless my visits and advice might have been at another time, the present was too fearful an occasion to suffer my doubts of their utility, or my reluctance to re-attempting what appeared a hopeless task, to weigh even against the lightest chance that a consciousness of his imminent danger might produce in him a more docile and tractable disposition. Accordingly I told the child to lead the way, and followed her in silence. She hurried rapidly through the long narrow street which forms the great thoroughfare of the town. The darkness of the hour, rendered still deeper by the close approach of the old-fashioned houses, which lowered in tall obscurity on either side of the way; the damp, dreary chill which renders the advance of morning peculiarly cheerless, combined with the object of my walk—to visit the death-bed of a presumptuous sinner, to endeavour, almost against my own conviction, to infuse a hope into the heart of a dying reprobate—a drunkard but too probably perishing under the consequences of some mad fit of intoxication; all these circumstances served to enhance the gloom and solemnity of my feelings, as I silently followed my little guide, who with quick steps traversed the uneven pavement of the main street. After a walk of about five minutes, she turned off into a narrow lane of that obscure and comfortless close which is to be found in almost all small old-fashioned towns, chill, without ventilation, reeking with all manner of offensive effluvia, and lined by dingy, smoky, sickly and pent-up buildings, frequently not only in a wretched but in a dangerous condition.

'Your father has changed his abode since I last visited him, and, I am afraid, much for the worse,' said I.

'Indeed he has, sir; but we must not complain,' replied she. 'We have to thank God that we have lodging and food, though it's poor enough, it is, your honour.'

Poor child! thought I. How many an older head might learn wisdom from thee—how many a luxurious philosopher, who is skilled to preach but not to suffer, might not thy patient words put to the blush! The manner and language of my companion were alike above her years and station; and, indeed, in all cases in which the cares and sorrows of life have anticipated their usual date, and have fallen, as they sometimes do, with melancholy prematurity to the lot of childhood, I have observed the result to have proved uniformly the same. A young mind, to which joy and indulgence have been strangers, and to which suffering and self-denial have been familiarized from the first, acquires a solidity and an elevation which no other discipline could have bestowed, and which, in the present case, communicated a striking but mournful peculiarity to the manners, even to the voice, of the child. We paused before a narrow, crazy door, which she opened by means of a latch, and we forthwith began to ascend the steep and broken stairs which led to the sick man's room.

As we mounted the flight after flight towards the garret-floor, I heard more and more distinctly the hurried talking of many voices. I could also distinguish the low sobbing of a female. On arriving upon the uppermost lobby, these sounds became fully audible.

'This way, your honour,' said my little conductress; at the same time, pushing open a door of patched and half-rotten plank, she admitted me into the squalid chamber of death and misery. But one candle, held in the fingers of a scared and haggard-looking child, was burning in the room, and that so dim that all was twilight or darkness except within its immediate influence. The general obscurity, however, served to throw into prominent and startling relief the death-bed and its occupant. The light fell with horrible clearness upon the blue and swollen features of the drunkard. I did not think it possible that a human countenance could look so terrific. The lips were black and drawn apart; the teeth were firmly set; the eyes a little unclosed, and nothing but the whites appearing. Every feature was fixed and livid, and the whole face wore a ghastly and rigid expression of despairing terror such as I never saw equalled. His hands were crossed upon his breast, and firmly clenched; while, as if to add to the corpse-like effect of the whole, some white cloths, dipped in water, were wound about the forehead and temples.

As soon as I could remove my eyes from this horrible spectacle, I observed my friend Dr D——, one of the most humane of a humane profession, standing by the bedside. He had been attempting, but unsuccessfully, to bleed the patient, and had now applied his finger to the pulse.

'Is there any hope?' I inquired in a whisper.

A shake of the head was the reply. There was a pause, while he continued to hold the wrist; but he waited in vain for the throb of life—it was not there: and when he let go the hand it fell stiffly back into its former position upon the other.

'The man is dead,' said the physician, as he turned from the bed where the terrible figure lay.

Dead! thought I, scarcely venturing to look upon the tremendous and revolting spectacle. Dead! without an hour for repentance, even a moment for reflection. Dead! without the rites which even the best should have. Was there a hope for him? The glaring eyeball, the grinning mouth, the distorted brow—that unutterable look in which a painter would have sought to embody the fixed despair of the nethermost hell—these were my answer.

The poor wife sat at a little distance, crying as if her heart would break—the younger children clustered round the bed, looking with wondering curiosity upon the form of death, never seen before.

When the first tumult of uncontrollable sorrow had passed away, availing myself of the solemnity and impressiveness of the scene, I desired the heart-stricken family to accompany me in prayer, and all knelt down while I solemnly and fervently repeated some of those prayers which appeared most applicable to the occasion. I employed myself thus in a manner which I trusted was not unprofitable, at least to the living, for about ten minutes; and having accomplished my task, I was the first to arise.

I looked upon the poor, sobbing, helpless creatures who knelt so humbly around me, and my heart bled for them. With a natural transition I turned my eyes from them to the bed in which the body lay; and, great God! what was the revulsion, the horror which I experienced on seeing the corpse-like, terrific thing seated half upright before me. The white cloths which had been wound about the head had now partly slipped from their position, and were hanging in grotesque festoons about the face and shoulders, while the distorted eyes leered from amid them—

'A sight to dream of, not to tell.'

I stood actually riveted to the spot. The figure nodded its

head and lifted its arm, I thought, with a menacing gesture. A thousand confused and horrible thoughts at once rushed upon my mind. I had often read that the body of a presumptuous sinner, who, during life, had been the willing creature of every satanic impulse, had been known, after the human tenant had deserted it, to become the horrible sport of demoniac possession.

I was roused by the piercing scream of the mother, who now, for the first time, perceived the change which had taken place. She rushed towards the bed, but, stunned by the shock and overcome by the conflict of violent emotions, before she reached it she fell prostrate upon the floor.

I am perfectly convinced that had I not been startled from the torpidity of horror in which I was bound by some powerful and arousing stimulant, I should have gazed upon this unearthly apparition until I had fairly lost my senses. As it was, however, the spell was broken—superstition gave way to reason: the man whom all believed to have been actually dead was living!

Dr D—— was instantly standing by the bedside, and upon examination he found that a sudden and copious flow of blood had taken place from the wound which the lancet had left; and this, no doubt, had effected his sudden and almost supernatural restoration to an existence from which all thought he had been for ever removed. The man was still speechless, but he seemed to understand the physician when he forbade his repeating the painful and fruitless attempts which he made to articulate, and he at once resigned himself quietly into his hands.

I left the patient with leeches upon his temples, and bleeding freely, apparently with little of the drowsiness which accompanies apoplexy. Indeed Dr D—— told me that he had never before witnessed a seizure which seemed to combine the symptoms of so many kinds, and yet which belonged to none of the recognized classes; it certainly was not apoplexy, catalepsy, nor *delirium tremens*, and yet it seemed, in some degree, to partake of the properties of all. It was strange, but stranger things are coming.

During two or three days Dr D—— would not allow

his patient to converse in a manner which could excite or exhaust him, with anyone; he suffered him merely as briefly as possible to express his immediate wants. And it was not until the fourth day after my early visit, the particulars of which I have just detailed, that it was thought expedient that I should see him, and then only because it appeared that his extreme importunity and impatience to meet me were likely to retard his recovery more than the mere exhaustion attendant upon a short conversation could possibly do. Perhaps, too, my friend entertained some hope that if by holy confession his patient's bosom were eased of the perilous stuff which no doubt oppressed it, his recovery would be more assured and rapid. It was then, as I have said, upon the fourth day after my first professional call that I found myself once more in the dreary chamber of want and sickness.

The man was in bed, and appeared low and restless. On my entering the room he raised himself in the bed, and muttered, twice or thrice:

'Thank God! thank God!'

I signed to those of his family who stood by to leave the room, and took a chair beside the bed. So soon as we were alone, he said, rather doggedly:

'There's no use in telling me of the sinfulness of bad ways—I know it all. I know where they lead to—I have seen everything about it with my own eyesight, as plain as I see you.' He rolled himself in the bed, as if to hide his face in the clothes; and then suddenly raising himself, he exclaimed with startling vehemence, 'Look, sir! there is no use in mincing the matter: I'm blasted with the fires of hell; I have been in hell. What do you think of that? In hell—I'm lost for ever— I have not a chance. I am damned already—damned—damned!'

The end of this sentence he actually shouted. His vehemence was perfectly terrific; he threw himself back, and laughed, and sobbed hysterically. I poured some water into a tea-cup, and gave it to him. After he had swallowed it, I told him if he had anything to communicate to do so as briefly as he could, and in a manner as little agitating to himself as possible; threatening at the same time, though I had no intention of doing so, to leave him at once in case he again gave way to such passionate excitement.

'It's only foolishness,' he continued, 'for me to try to thank you for coming to such a villain as myself at all. It's no use for me to wish good to you, or to bless you; for such as me has no blessings to give.'

I told him that I had but done my duty, and urged him to proceed to the matter which weighed upon his mind. He then spoke nearly as follows:

'I came in drunk on Friday night last, and got to my bed here; I don't remember how. Sometime in the night it seemed to me I wakened, and feeling uneasy in myself, I got up out of the bed. I wanted the fresh air; but I would not make a noise to open the window, for fear I'd waken the crathurs. It was very dark and throublesome to find the door; but at last I did get it, and I groped my way out, and went down as asy as I could. I felt quite sober, and I counted the steps one after another, as I was going down, that I might not stumble at the bottom.

'When I came to the first landing-place—God be about us always!—the floor of it sunk under me, and I went down —down—down, till the senses almost left me. I do not know how long I was falling, but it seemed to me a great while. When I came rightly to myself at last, I was sitting near the top of a great table; and I could not see the end of it, if it had any, it was so far off. And there was men beyond reckoning sitting down all along by it, at each side, as far as I could see at all. I did not know at first was it in the open air; but there was a close smothering in it that was not natural. And there was a kind of light that my eyesight never saw before, red and unsteady; and I did not see for a long time where it was coming from, until I looked straight up, and then I seen that it came from great balls of blood-coloured fire that were rolling high overhead with a sort of rushing, trembling sound, and I perceived that they shone on the ribs of a great roof of rock that was arched overhead instead of the sky. When I seen this, scarce knowing what I did, I got up, and I said, "I have no right to be here; I must go." And the man that was sitting at my left hand only smiled, and said, "Sit down again; you can *never* leave this place." And his voice was weaker than any child's voice I ever heerd; and when he was done speaking he smiled again.

'Then I spoke out very loud and bold, and I said, "In the name of God, let me out of this bad place." And there was a great man that I did not see before, sitting at the end of the table that I was near; and he was taller than twelve men, and his face was very proud and terrible to look at. And he stood up and stretched out his hand before him; and when he stood up, all that was there, great and small, bowed down with a sighing sound; and a dread came on my heart, and he looked at me, and I could not speak. I felt I was his own, to do what he liked with, for I knew at once who he was; and he said, "If you promise to return, you may depart for a season;" and the voice he spoke with was terrible and mournful, and the echoes of it went rolling and swelling down the endless cave, and mixing with the trembling of the fire overhead; so that when he sat down there was a sound after him, all through the place, like the roaring of a furnace. And I said, with all the strength I had, "I promise to come back—in God's name let me go!"

'And with that I lost the sight and hearing of all that was there, and when my senses came to me again I was sitting in the bed with the blood all over me, and you and the rest praying around the room.'

Here he paused, and wiped away the chill drops which hung upon his forehead.

I remained silent for some moments. The vision which he had just described struck my imagination not a little, for this was long before Vathek and the 'Hall of Eblis' had delighted the world; and the description which he gave had, as I received it, all the attractions of novelty beside the impressiveness which always belongs to the narration of an *eye-witness*, whether in the body or in the spirit, of the scenes which he describes. There was something, too, in the stern horror with which the man related these things, and in the incongruity of his description with the vulgarly received notions of the great place of punishment, and of its presiding spirit, which struck my mind with awe, almost with fear. At length he said, with an expression of horrible, imploring earnestness which I shall never forget:

'Well, sir, is there any hope; is there any chance at all? or is my soul pledged and promised away for ever? is it gone out of my power? must I go back to the place?'

In answering him, I had no easy task to perform; for however clear might be my internal conviction of the groundlessness of his fears, and however strong my scepticism respecting the reality of what he had described, I nevertheless felt that his impression to the contrary, and his humility and terror resulting from it, might be made available as no mean engines in the work of his conversion from profligacy, and of his restoration to decent habits and to religious feeling.

I therefore told him that he was to regard his dream rather in the light of a warning than in that of a prophecy; that our salvation depended not upon the word or deed of a moment, but upon the habits of a life; that, in fine, if he at once discarded his idle companions and evil habits, and firmly adhered to a sober, industrious and religious course of life, the powers of darkness might claim his soul in vain, for that there were higher and firmer pledges than human tongue could utter, which promised salvation to him who should repent and lead a new life.

I left him much comforted, and with a promise to return upon the next day. I did so, and found him much more cheerful, and without any remains of the dogged sullenness which I suppose had arisen from his despair. His promises of amendment were given in that tone of deliberate earnestness which belongs to deep and solemn determination; and it was with no small delight that I observed, after repeated visits, that his good resolutions, so far from failing, did but gather strength by time; and when I saw that man shake off the idle and debauched companions whose society had for years formed alike his amusement and his ruin, and revive his long-discarded habits of industry and sobriety, I said within myself, There is something more in all this than the operation of an idle dream.

One day, some time after his perfect restoration to health,

I was surprised, on ascending the stairs for the purpose of visiting this man, to find him busily employed in nailing down some planks upon the landing-place, through which, at the commencement of his mysterious vision, it seemed to him that he had sunk. I perceived at once that he was strengthening the floor with a view to securing himself against such a catastrophe, and could scarcely forbear a smile as I bid 'God bless his work.'

He perceived my thoughts, I suppose, for he immediately said:

'I can never pass over that floor without trembling. I'd leave this house if I could, but I can't find another lodging in the town so cheap, and I'll not take a better till I've paid off all my debts, please God; but I could not be asy in my mind till I made it as safe as I could. You'll hardly believe me, your honour, that while I'm working, maybe a mile away, my heart is in a flutter the whole way back with the bare thoughts of the two little steps I have to walk upon this bit of a floor. So it's no wonder, sir, I'd thry to make it sound and firm with any idle timber I have.'

I applauded his resolution to pay off his debts, and the steadiness with which he pursued his plans of conscientious economy, and passed on.

Many months elapsed, and still there appeared no alteration in his resolutions of amendment. He was a good workman, and with his better habits he recovered his former extensive and profitable employment. Everything seemed to promise comfort and respectability. I have little more to add, and that shall be told quickly. I had one evening met Pat Connell, as he returned from his work, and as usual, after a mutual, and on his side respectful salutation, I spoke a few words of encouragement and approval. I left him industrious, active, healthy—when next I saw him, not three days after, he was a corpse.

The circumstances which marked the event of his death were somewhat strange—I might say fearful. The unfortunate man had accidentally met an old friend just returned, after a long absence; and in a moment of excitement, forgetting everything in the warmth of his joy, he yielded to his

urgent invitation to accompany him into a public-house, which
lay close by the spot where the encounter had taken place.
Connell, however, previously to entering the room, had announced his determination to take nothing more than the
strictest temperance would warrant.

But oh! who can describe the inveterate tenacity with
which a drunkard's habits cling to him through life? He
may repent, he may reform, he may look with actual abhor-
rence upon his past profligacy; but amid all this reformation
and compunction, who can tell the moment in which the
base and ruinous propensity may not recur, triumphing over
resolution, remorse, shame, everything, and prostrating its
victim once more in all that is destructive and revolting in
that fatal vice?

The wretched man left the place in a state of utter intoxication. He was brought home nearly insensible, and placed
in his bed. The younger part of the family retired to rest much
after their usual hour; but the poor wife remained up sitting
by the fire, too much grieved and shocked at the occurrence
of what she had so little expected, to settle to rest. Fatigue,
however, at length overcame her, and she sank gradually into
an uneasy slumber. She could not tell how long she had
remained in this state; but when she awakened, and immediately on opening her eyes, she perceived by the faint red
light of the smouldering turf embers two persons, one of whom
she recognized as her husband, noiselessly gliding out of the
room.

'Pat, darling, where are you going?' said she.

There was no answer—the door closed after them; but
in a moment she was startled and terrified by a loud and
heavy crash, as if some ponderous body had been hurled down
the stair.

Much alarmed, she started up, and going to the head of
the staircase she called repeatedly upon her husband, but in
vain.

She returned to the room, and with the assistance of her
daughter whom I had occasion to mention before, she succeeded in finding and lighting a candle, with which she hurried
again to the head of the staircase.

At the bottom lay what seemed to be a bundle of clothes, heaped together, motionless, lifeless—it was her husband. In going down the stairs, for what purpose can never now be known, he had fallen helplessly and violently to the bottom, and, coming head foremost, the spine of the neck had been dislocated by the shock, and instant death must have ensued.

The body lay upon that landing-place to which his dream had referred.

It is scarcely worth endeavouring to clear up a single point in a narrative where all is mystery; yet I could not help suspecting that the second figure which had been seen in the room by Connell's wife on the night of his death might have been no other than his own shadow.

I suggested this solution of the difficulty; but she told me that the unknown person had been considerably in advance of her husband, and on reaching the door had turned back as if to communicate something to his companion.

It was, then, a mystery.

Was the dream verified?—whither had the disembodied spirit sped? who can say? We know not. But I left the house of death that day in a state of horror which I could not describe. It seemed to me that I was scarce awake. I heard and saw everything as if under the spell of a nightmare. The coincidence was terrible.

LOUGH FOYLE

'Lough Foyle' means 'the borrowed lake', for in old times there were two weird sisters dwelling beyond the Shannon who were skilled in necromancy. And the elder sister said to the younger:

'Give me the loan of your silver lake, for I have none, and I promise to restore it to you next Monday.'

So the younger, being good-natured, rolled up the lake in a sheet and despatched it over hills and dales to her sister. But when the time came for return, the elder sister, being deceitful and cunning, made answer to the messenger sent for it:

'Truly, I said Monday, but I meant the Day of Judgment. So I shall keep the lake till then.'

And the lake therefore remains in her country to this day, while the great hollow whence it was taken can still be seen in Connaught, bare and barren, waiting for the waters that never will return.

WILDGOOSE LODGE

WILLIAM CARLETON

I had read the anonymous summons, but, from its general import, I believed it to be one of those special meetings convened for some purpose affecting the usual objects and proceedings of the body; at least, the terms in which it was conveyed to me had nothing extraordinary or mysterious in them beyond the simple fact that it was not to be a general but a select meeting. This mark of confidence flattered me, and I determined to attend punctually. I was, it is true, desired to keep the circumstance entirely to myself; but there was nothing startling in this, for I had often received summonses of a similar nature. I therefore resolved to attend, according to the letter of my instructions, 'on the next night, at the solemn hour of midnight, to deliberate and act upon such matters as should then and there be submitted to my consideration.' The morning after I received this message I arose and resumed my usual occupations; but, from whatever cause it may have proceeded, I felt a sense of approaching evil hang heavily upon me: the beats of my pulse were languid, and an undefinable feeling of anxiety pervaded my whole spirit; even my face was pale, and my eye so heavy that my father and brothers concluded me to be ill— an opinion which I thought at the time to be correct, for I felt exactly that kind of depression which precedes a severe fever. I could not understand what I experienced, nor can I yet, except by supposing that there is in human nature some mysterious faculty by which, in coming calamities, the dread of some fearful evil is anticipated, and that it is possible to catch a dark presentiment of the sensations which they subsequently produce. For my part, I can neither analyse nor define it; but on that day I knew it by painful experience, and so have a thousand others in similar circumstances.

It was about the middle of winter. The day was gloomy and tempestuous almost beyond any other I remember. Dark clouds rolled over the hills about me, and a close, sleet-like rain fell in slanting drifts that chased each other rapidly towards the earth on the course of the blast. The outlying cattle sought the closest and calmest corners of the fields for shelter; the trees and young groves were tossed about, for the wind was so unusually high that it swept in hollow gusts through them with that hoarse murmur which deepens so powerfully on the mind the sense of dreariness and desolation.

As the shades of night fell, the storm, if possible, increased. The moon was half gone, and only a few stars were visible by glimpses, as a rush of wind left a temporary opening in the sky. I had determined, if the storm should not abate, to incur any penalty rather than attend the meeting; but the appointed hour was distant, and I resolved to be decided by the future state of the night.

Ten o'clock came, but still there was no change; eleven passed, and on opening the door to observe if there were any likelihood of its clearing up, a blast of wind, mingled with rain, nearly blew me off my feet. At length it was approaching to the hour of midnight; and on examining a third time, I found it had calmed a little, and no longer rained.

I instantly got my oak stick, muffled myself in my greatcoat, strapped my hat about my ears, and, as the place of meeting was only a quarter of a mile distant, I presently set out.

The appearance of the heavens was lowering and angry, particularly in that point where the light of the moon fell against the clouds, from a seeming chasm in them, through which alone she was visible. The edges of this chasm were faintly bronzed, but the dense body of the masses that hung piled on each side of her was black and impenetrable to sight. In no other point of the heavens was there any part of the sky visible; a deep veil of clouds overhung the horizon, yet was the light sufficient to give occasional glimpses of the rapid shifting which took place in this dark canopy, and of the tempestuous agitation with which the midnight storm swept to and fro beneath it.

At length I arrived at a long slated house, situated in a solitary part of the neighbourhood; a little below it ran a small stream, which was now swollen above its banks, and rushing with mimic roar over the flat meadows beside it. The appearance of the bare slated building in such a night was particularly sombre, and to those, like me, who knew the purpose to which it was usually devoted, it was, or ought to have been, peculiarly so. There it stood, silent and gloomy, without any appearance of human life or enjoyment about or within it. As I approached, the moon once more had broken out of the clouds, and shone dimly upon the wet, glittering slates and windows with a deathlike lustre, that gradually faded away as I left the point of observation and entered the folding-door. It was the parish chapel.

The scene which presented itself here was in keeping not only with the external appearance of the house, but with the darkness, the storm, and the hour, which was now a little after midnight. About eighty persons were sitting in dead silence upon the circular steps of the altar. They did not seem to move; and as I entered and advanced the echo of my footsteps rang through the building with a lonely distinctness which added to the solemnity and mystery of the circumstances about me. The windows were secured with shutters on the inside, and on the altar a candle was lighted, which burned dimly amid the surrounding darkness, and lengthened the shadow of the altar itself, and those of six or seven persons who stood on its upper steps, until they mingled in the obscurity which shrouded the lower end of the chapel. The faces of the men who sat on the altar steps were not distinctly visible, yet their prominent and more characteristic features were in sufficient relief, and I observed that some of the most malignant and reckless spirits in the parish were assembled. In the eyes of those who stood at the altar, I could perceive gleams of some latent and ferocious purpose, kindled, as I soon observed, into a fiercer expression of vengeance by the additional excitement of ardent spirits, with which they had stimulated themselves to a point of determination that mocked at the apprehension of all future responsibility, either in this world or the next.

The welcome which I received on joining them was far different from the boisterous good-humour that used to mark our greetings on other occasions: just a nod of the head from this or that person, on the part of those *who sat*, with a *ghud dhemur tha thu?*[1] in a suppressed voice, even below a common whisper; but from the standing group, who were evidently the projectors of the enterprise, I received a convulsive grasp of the hand, accompanied by a fierce and desperate look that seemed to search my eye and countenance, to try if I were a person not likely to shrink from whatever they had resolved to execute. It is surprising to think of the powerful expression which a moment of intense interest or great danger is capable of giving to the eye, the features, and the slightest actions, especially in those whose station in society does not require them to constrain nature, by the force of social courtesies, into habits that conceal their natural emotions. None of the standing group spoke; but as each of them wrung my hand in silence his eye was fixed on mine with an expression of drunken confidence and secrecy, and an insolent determination not to be gainsayed without peril. If looks could be translated with certainty, they seemed to say, 'We are bound upon a project of vengeance, and if you do not join us, remember that we *can* revenge.' Along with this grasp they did not forget to remind me of the common bond by which we were united, for each man gave me the secret grip of Ribbonism in a manner that made the joints of my fingers ache for some minutes afterwards.

There was one present, however—the highest in authority—whose actions and demeanour were calm and unexcited. He seemed to labour under no unusual influence whatever, but evinced a serenity so placid and philosophical that I attributed the silence of the sitting group, and the restraint which curbed in the out-breaking passions of those who *stood,* entirely to his presence. He was a schoolmaster, who taught his daily school in that chapel, and acted also on Sunday in the capacity of clerk to the priest—an excellent and amiable old man, who knew little of his illegal connections and atrocious conduct.

When the ceremonies of brotherly recognition and friendship were past, the captain (by which title I shall designate the last-mentioned person) stooped, and raising a jar of whisky on the corner of the altar, held a wine-glass to its neck, which he filled, and, with a calm nod, handed it to me to drink. I shrunk back,

[1] How are you?

with an instinctive horror at the profaneness of such an act, in
the house, and on the altar, of God, and peremptorily refused to
taste the proffered draught. He smiled mildly at what he considered my superstition, and added quietly, and in a low voice,
'You'll be wantin' it, I'm thinkin', afther the wettin' you got.'

'Wet or dry,' said I——

'Stop, man!' he replied, in the same tone; 'spake low.
But why wouldn't you take the whisky? Sure there's as holy
people to the fore as you; didn't they all take it? An' I wish
we may never do worse nor dhrink a harmless glass o' whisky
to keep the cowld out, anyway.'

'Well,' said I 'I'll jist trust to God and the consequences
for the cowld, Paddy, ma bouchal; but a blessed dhrop of it
won't be crossin' my lips, avick; so no more ghosther about it—
dhrink it yourself, if you like. Maybe you want it as much as I
do; wherein I've the patthern of a good big coat upon me, so
thick, your sowl, that if it was rainin' bullocks a dhrop wouldn't
get under the nap of it.'

He gave me a calm but keen glance as I spoke.

'Well, Jim,' said he, 'it's a good comrade you've got for the
weather that's in it; but, in the manetime, to set you a dacent
patthern, I'll just take this myself'—saying which, with the jar
still upon its side, and the forefinger of his left hand in its neck,
he swallowed the spirits. 'It's the first I dhrank to-night,' he
added, 'nor would I dhrink it now, only to show you that I've
heart an' spirit to do the thing that we're all bound an' sworn
to, when the proper time comes;' after which he laid down the
glass, and turned up the jar, with much coolness, upon the altar.

During our conversation those who had been summoned to
this mysterious meeting were pouring in fast; and as each
person approached the altar he received from one to two or
three glasses of whisky, according as he chose to limit himself; but, to do them justice, there were not a few of those
present who, in spite of their own desire and the captain's
express invitation, refused to taste it in the house of God's
worship. Such, however, as were scrupulous he afterwards
recommended to take it on the outside of the chapel door,
which they did, as by that means, the sacrilege of the act was
supposed to be evaded.

About one o'clock they were all assembled except six; at least so the captain asserted on looking at a written paper.

'Now, boys,' said he, in the same low voice, 'we are all present except the thraitors whose names I am goin' to read to you; not that we are to count thim thraitors, till we know whether or not it was in their power to come. Anyhow, the night's terrible—but, boys, you're to know that neither fire nor wather is to prevint yees, when duly summoned to attind a meeting—particularly whin the summons is widout a name, as you have been told that there is always something of conse-quence to be done *thin*.'

He then read out the names of those who were absent, in order that the real cause of their absence might be ascertained, declaring that they would be dealt with accordingly. After this, with his usual caution, he shut and bolted the door, and having put the key in his pocket, ascended the steps of the altar, and for some time traversed the little platform from which the priest usually addresses the congregation.

Until this night I had never contemplated the man's counten-ance with any particular interest; but as he walked the platform I had an opportunity of observing him more closely. He was slight in person, apparently not thirty; and, on a first view, appeared to have nothing remarkable in his dress or features. I, however, was not the only person whose eyes were fixed upon him at that moment; in fact, every one present observed him with equal interest, for hitherto he had kept the object of the meeting perfectly secret, and of course we all felt anxious to know it. It was while he traversed the platform that I scrutinised his features with a hope, if possible, to glean from them some evidence of what was passing within him. I could, however, mark but little, and that little was at first rather from the intelligence which seemed to subsist between him and those whom I have already mentioned as *standing* against the altar than from any indication of his own. Their gleaming eyes were fixed upon him with an intensity of savage and demon-like hope which blazed out in flashes of malignant triumph, as, upon turning, he threw a cool but rapid glance at them, to intimate the progress he was making in the subject to which he devoted the undivided energies of his mind. But in the course of his

111

meditation I could observe, on one or two occasions, a dark shade come over his countenance, that contracted his brow into a deep furrow, and it was then, for the first time, that I saw the Satanic expression of which his face, by a very slight motion of its muscles, was capable. His hands, during this silence, closed and opened convulsively; his eyes shot out two or three baleful glances, first to his confederates, and afterwards vacantly into the deep gloom of the lower part of the chapel; his teeth ground against each other like those of a man whose revenge burns to reach a distant enemy; and finally, after having wound himself up to a certain determination, his features relapsed into their original calm and undisturbed expression.

At this moment a loud laugh, having something supernatural in it, rang out wildly from the darkness of the chapel; he stopped, and putting his open hand over his brows, peered down into the gloom, and said calmly, in Irish, *'Bee dhu husth; ha nihl anam inh*—hold your tongue; it is not yet the time.'

Every eye was now directed to the same spot, but, in consequence of its distance from the dim light on the altar, none could perceive the person from whom the laugh proceeded. It was by this time near two o'clock in the morning.

He now stood for a few moments on the platform, and his chest heaved with a depth of anxiety equal to the difficulty of the design he wished to accomplish.

'Brothers,' said he—'for we are all brothers—sworn upon all that's blessed an' holy to obey whatever them that's over us, *manin' among ourselves,*[1] wishes us to do—are you now ready, in the name of God, upon whose althar I stand, to fulfil yer oaths?'

The words were scarcely uttered when those who had *stood* beside the altar during the night sprang from their places, and descending its steps rapidly, turned round, and raising their arms, exclaimed, 'By all that's sacred an' holy, we're willin'.'

In the meantime those who *sat* upon the steps of the altar instantly rose, and, following the example of those who had just spoken, exclaimed after them, 'To be sure—by all that's sacred an' holy, we're willin'.'

[1] In opposition to the constituted authorities.

'Now, boys,' said the captain, 'aren't yees big fools for your pains? an' one of yees doesn't know what I mane.'

'You're our captain,' said one of those who had stood at the altar, 'an' has yer ordhers from higher quarthers; of coorse, whatever ye command upon us we're bound to obey you in.'

'Well,' said he, smiling, 'I only wanted to thry yees; an' by the oath yees tuck, there's not a captain in the county has as good a right to be proud of his min as I have. Well, yees won't rue it, maybe, when the right time comes; and for that same rason every one of yees must have a glass from the jar; thim that won't dhrink it *in* the chapel can dhrink it *widout*; an' here goes to open the door for them.'

He then distributed another glass to every man who would accept it, and brought the jar afterwards to the chapel door, to satisfy the scruples of those who would not drink within. When this was performed, and all duly excited, he proceeded—

'Now, brothers, you are solemnly sworn to obey me, and I'm sure there's no thraithur here that ud parjure himself for a thrifle; but *I'm* sworn to obey them that's above me, manin' still among ourselves; an' to show you that I don't scruple to do it, here goes!'

He then turned round, and taking the Missal between his hands, placed it upon the altar. Hitherto every word was uttered in a low, precautionary tone; but on grasping the book he again turned round, and looking upon his confederates with the same Satanic expression which marked his countenance before, exclaimed, in a voice of deep determination—

'By this sacred an' holy book of God, I will perform the action which we have met this night to accomplish, be that what it may; an' this I swear upon God's book an' God's althar!'

On concluding he struck the book violently with his open hand. At this moment the candle which burned before him went suddenly out, and the chapel was wrapped in pitchy darkness; the sound as if of rushing wings fell upon our ears, and fifty voices dwelt upon the last words of his oath with wild and supernatural tones, that seemed to echo and to mock what he had sworn. There was a pause, and an exclamation of horror from all present. But the captain was too cool and steady to be disconcerted. He immediately groped about until he got the candle, and proceeding calmly to a remote corner of the chapel, took up a half-burned turf which lay there, and, after some trouble, succeeded in lighting it again. He then explained what had taken place; which indeed was easily done, as the candle happened to be extinguished by a pigeon which sat directly above it. The chapel, I should have observed, was at this time, like many country chapels, unfinished inside, and the pigeons of a neighbouring dove-cote had built nests among the rafters of the unceiled room; which circumstance also explained the rushing of the wings, for the birds had been affrighted by the sudden loudness of the noise. The mocking voices were nothing but the echoes, rendered naturally more awful by the scene, the mysterious object of the meeting, and the solemn hour of the night.

When the candle was again lighted, and these startling circumstances accounted for, the persons whose vengeance had been deepening more and more during the night rushed to the altar in a body, where each, in a voice trembling with passionate eagerness, repeated the oath; and as every word was pronounced the same echoes heightened the wildness of the horrible ceremony by their long and unearthly tones. The countenances of these human tigers were livid with suppressed rage; their knit brows, compressed lips, and kindled eyes fell under the dim light of the taper with an expression calculated to sicken any heart not absolutely diabolical.

As soon as this dreadful rite was completed we were again startled by several loud bursts of laughter, which proceeded from the lower darkness of the chapel, and the captain, on hearing them, turned to the place, and, reflecting for a moment, said in Irish, '*Gutsho nish, avohelhee*—come hither now, boys.'

A rush immediately took place from the corner in which they had secreted themselves all the night; and seven men appeared, whom we instantly recognised as brothers and cousins of certain persons who had been convicted some time before for breaking into the house of an honest poor man in the neighbourhood, from whom, after having treated him with barbarous violence, they took away such fire-arms as he kept for his own protection.

It was evidently not the captain's intention to have produced these persons until the oath should have been generally taken, but the exulting mirth with which they enjoyed the success of his scheme betrayed them, and put him to the necessity of bringing them forward somewhat before the concerted moment.

The scene which now took place was beyond all power of description: peals of wild, fiend-like yells rang through the chapel, as the party which *stood* on the altar and that which had crouched in the darkness met; wringing of hands, leaping in triumph, striking sticks and fire-arms against the ground and the altar itself, dancing and cracking of fingers, marked the triumph of some hellish determination. Even the captain for a time was unable to restrain their fury; but at length he mounted the platform before the altar once more, and, with a stamp of his foot, recalled their attention to himself and the matter in hand.

'Boys,' said he, 'enough of this, and too much; an' well for us it is that the chapel is in a lonely place, or our foolish noise might do us no good. Let thim that swore so manfully jist now stand a one side, till the rest kiss the book, one by one.'

The proceedings, however, had by this time taken too fearful a shape for even the captain to compel them to a blindfold oath. The first man he called flatly refused to answer until he should hear the nature of the service that was required. This was echoed by the remainder, who, taking courage from the firmness of this person, declared generally that until they first knew the business they were to execute none of them would take the oath. The captain's lip quivered slightly, and his brow again became knit with the same hellish expression, which I have remarked gave him so much the appearance of an embodied fiend; but this speedily passed away, and was succeeded by a malignant sneer, in which lurked, if there ever did in a sneer, 'a laughing devil,' calmly, determinedly atrocious.

'It wasn't worth yer whiles to refuse the oath,' said he mildly, 'for the truth is, I had next to nothing for yees to do. Not a hand, maybe, would have to *rise*, only jist to look on, an' if any resistance would be made, to show yourselves; yer numbers would soon make them see that resistance would be no use whatever in the present case. At all evints, the oath of *secrecy must* be taken, or woe be to him that will refuse *that*; he won't know the day, nor the hour, nor the minute, when he'll be made a spatchcock ov.'

He then turned round, and, placing his right hand on the Missal swore, 'In the presence of God, and before his holy altar, that whatever might take place that night he would keep secret from man or mortal, except the priest, and that neither bribery, nor imprisonment, nor death would wring it from his heart.'

Having done this, he again struck the book violently, as if to confirm the energy with which he swore, and then calmly descending the steps, stood with a serene countenance, like a man conscious of having performed a good action. As this oath did not pledge those who refused to take the other to the perpetration of any specific crime, it was readily taken by all present. Preparations were then made to execute what was intended; the half-burned turf was placed in a little pot; another glass of whisky was distributed; and the door being locked by the captain, who kept the key as parish clerk and master, the crowd departed silently from the chapel.

The moment those who lay in the darkness during the night made their appearance at the altar, we knew at once the persons we were to visit; for, as I said before, they were related to the miscreants whom one of those persons had convicted, in consequence of their midnight attack upon himself and his family. The captain's object in keeping them unseen was that those present, not being aware of the duty about to be imposed on them, might have less hesitation about swearing to its fulfilment. Our conjectures were correct, for on leaving the chapel we directed our steps to the house in which this devoted man resided.

The night was still stormy, but without rain; it was rather dark too, though not so as to prevent us from seeing the clouds careering swiftly through the air. The dense curtain which had overhung and obscured the horizon was now broken, and large sections of the sky were clear, and thinly studded with stars that looked dim and watery, as did indeed the whole firmament; for in some places black clouds were still visible, threatening a continuance of tempestuous weather. The road appeared washed and gravelly; every dike was full of yellow water; and every little rivulet and larger stream dashed its hoarse music in our ears; every blast, too, was cold, fierce, and wintry, sometimes driving us back to a standstill, and again, when a turn in the road would bring it in our backs, whirling us along for a few steps with involuntary rapidity. At length the fated dwelling became visible, and a short consultation was held in a sheltered place between the captain and the two parties who seemed so eager for its destruction. The fire-arms were now loaded, and their bayonets and short pikes, the latter shod and pointed with iron, were also got ready. The live coal which was brought in the small pot had become extinguished; but to remedy this two or three persons from a remote part of the country entered a cabin on the wayside, and under pretence of lighting their own and their comrades' pipes, procured a coal of fire, for so they called a lighted turf. From the time we left the chapel until this moment a profound silence had been maintained—a circumstance which, when I considered the number of persons present, and the mysterious and dreaded object of their journey, had a most appalling effect upon my spirits.

At length we arrived within fifty perches of the house, walking in a compact body, and with as little noise as possible; but it seemed as if the very elements had conspired to frustrate our design, for on advancing within the shade of the farm-hedge, two or three persons found themselves up to the middle in water, and on stooping to ascertain more accurately the state of the place, we could see nothing but one immense sheet of it —spread like a lake over the meadows which surrounded the spot we wished to reach.

Fatal night! The very recollection of it, when associated with the fearful tempests of the elements, grows, if that were possible, yet more wild and revolting. Had we been engaged in any innocent or benevolent enterprise, there was something in our situation just then that had a touch of interest in it to a mind imbued with a relish for the savage beauties of nature. There we stood, about a hundred and thirty in number, our dark forms bent forward, peering into the dusky expanse of water, with its dim gleams of reflected light, broken by the weltering of the mimic waves into ten thousand fragments, whilst the few stars that overhung it in the firmament appeared to shoot through it in broken lines, and to be multiplied fifty-fold in the gloomy mirror on which we gazed.

Over us was a stormy sky, and around us a darkness through which we could only distinguish, in outline, the nearest objects, whilst the wind swept strongly and dismally upon us. When it was discovered that the common pathway to the house was inundated, we were about to abandon our object and return home. The captain, however, stooped down low for a moment, and, almost closing his eyes, looked along the surface of the waters, and then, raising himself very calmly, said, in his usual quiet tone, 'Yees needn't go back, boys—I've found a way; jist follow me.'

He immediately took a more circuitous direction, by which we reached a causeway that had been raised for the purpose of giving a free passage to and from the house during such inundations as the present. Along this we had advanced more than half way when we discovered a breach in it, which, as afterwards appeared, had that night been made by the strength of the flood. This, by means of our sticks and pikes, we found to be about three feet deep and eight yards broad. Again we were at a loss how to proceed, when the fertile brain of the captain devised a method of crossing it.

'Boys,' said he, 'of coorse you've all played at leap-frog; very well, strip and go in, a dozen of you, lean one upon the back of another from this to the opposite bank, where one must stand facing the outside man, both their shoulders agin one another, that the outside man may be supported. Then *we* can creep over you; an' a dacent bridge you'll be, anyway.'

This was the work of only a few minutes, and in less than ten we were all safely over.

Merciful heaven! how I sicken at the recollection of what is to follow! On reaching the dry bank, we proceeded instantly, and in profound silence, to the house; the captain divided us into companies, and then assigned to each division its proper station. The two parties who had been so vindictive all the night he kept about himself; for of those who were present they only were in his confidence, and knew his nefarious purpose; their number was about fifteen. Having made these dispositions, he, at the head of about five of them, approached the house on the windy side, for the fiend possessed a coolness which enabled him to seize upon every possible advantage. That he had combustibles about him was evident, for in less than fifteen minutes nearly one-half of the house was enveloped in flames. On seeing this the others rushed over to the spot where he and his gang were standing, and remonstrated earnestly, but in vain; the flames now burst forth with renewed violence, and as they flung their strong light upon the faces of the foremost group, I think hell itself could hardly present anything more Satanic than their countenances, now worked up into a paroxysm of infernal triumph at their own revenge. The captain's look had lost all its calmness, every feature started out into distinct malignity, the curve in his brow was deep, and ran up to the root of the hair, dividing his face into two segments, that did not seem to have been designed for each other. His lips were half open, and the corners of his mouth a little brought back on each side, like those of a man expressing intense hatred and triumph over an enemy who is in the death struggle under his grasp. His eyes blazed from beneath his knit eyebrows with a fire that seemed to be lighted up in the infernal pit itself. It is unnecessary and only painful to describe the rest of his gang; demons might have been proud of such horrible visages as they exhibited—for they worked under all the power of hatred, revenge, and joy; and these passions blended into one terrible scowl, enough almost to blast any human eye that would venture to look upon it.

When the others atttempted to intercede for the lives of the inmates, there were at least fifteen guns and pistols levelled at them.

'Another word,' said the captain, 'an' you're a corpse where you stand, or the first man who will dare to spake for them; no, no, it wasn't to spare them we came here. "No mercy" is the password for the night, an' by the sacred oath I swore beyant in the chapel, any one among yees that will attempt to show it will find none at my hand. Surround the house, boys, I tell ye; I hear them stirring. "No quarther—no mercy," is the ordher of the night.'

Such was his command over these misguided creatures that

in an instant there was a ring round the house to prevent the escape of the unhappy inmates, should the raging element give them time to attempt it; for none present durst withdraw themselves from the scene, not only from an apprehension of the captain's present vengeance, or that of his gang, but because they knew that, even had they then escaped, an early and certain death awaited them from a quarter against which they had no means of defence. The hour was now about half-past two o'clock. Scarcely had the last words escaped from the captain's lips, when one of the windows of the house was broken, and a human head, having the hair in a blaze, was descried, apparently a woman's, if one might judge by the profusion of burning tresses, and the softness of the tones, notwithstanding that it called, or rather shrieked aloud, for help and mercy. The only reply to this was the whoop from the captain and his gang of 'No mercy—no mercy!' and that instant the former and one of the latter rushed to the spot, and ere the action could be perceived the head was transfixed with a bayonet and a pike, both having entered it together. The word mercy was divided in her mouth; a short silence ensued; the head hung down on the window, but was instantly tossed back into the flames!

This action occasioned a cry of horror from all present, except the *gang* and their leader, which startled and enraged the latter so much that he ran towards one of them, and had his bayonet, now reeking with the blood of its innocent victim, raised to plunge it in his body, when, dropping the point, he said in a piercing whisper, that hissed in the ears of all, 'It's no use *now*, you know; if one's to hang, all will hang; so our safest way, you persave, is to lave none of them to tell the story. Ye *may* go now, if you wish; but it won't save a hair of your heads. You cowardly set! I knew if I had tould yees the sport that none of yees, except my *own* boys, would come, so I jist played a thrick upon you; but remember what you are sworn to, and stand to the oath ye tuck.'

Unhappily, notwithstanding the wetness of the preceding weather, the materials of the house were extremely combustible; the whole dwelling was now one body of glowing flame, yet the shouts and shrieks within rose awfully above its crackling and the voice of the storm, for the wind once more blew in gusts and with great violence. The doors and windows were all torn open, and such of those within as had escaped the flames rushed towards them, for the purpose of further escape, and of claiming mercy at the hands of their destroyers; but whenever they appeared the unearthly cry of 'NO MERCY' rung upon their ears for a moment, and for a moment only, for they were flung back at the points of the weapons which the demons had brought with them to make the work of vengeance more certain.

As yet there were many persons in the house whose cry for life was strong as despair, and who clung to it with all the awakened powers of reason and instinct. The ear of man could hear nothing so strongly calculated to stifle the demon of cruelty and revenge within him as the long and wailing shrieks which rose beyond the elements in tones that were carried off rapidly upon the blast, until they died away in the darkness that lay behind the surrounding hills. Had not the house been in a solitary situation, and the hour the dead of night, any person sleeping within a moderate distance must have heard them, for such a cry of sorrow rising into a yell of despair was almost sufficient to have awakened the dead. It was lost, however, upon the hearts and ears that heard it: to them, though in justice be it said, to only comparatively a few of them, it was as delightful as the tones of soft and entrancing music.

The claims of the surviving sufferers were now modified: they supplicated merely to suffer death *by the weapons of their enemies*; they were willing to bear that, provided they should be allowed to escape from the flames; but no—the horrors of the conflagration were calmly and malignantly gloried in by their merciless assassins, who deliberately flung them back into all their tortures. In the course of a few minutes a man appeared upon the side-wall of the house, nearly naked; his figure, as he stood against the sky in horrible relief, was so finished a picture of woe-begone agony and supplication that it is yet as distinct in my memory as if I were again present at the scene. Every muscle, now in motion by the powerful agitation of his sufferings, stood out upon his limbs and neck, giving him an appearance of desperate strength, to which by this time he must have been wrought up; the perspiration poured from his frame, and the veins and arteries of his neck were inflated to a surprising thickness. Every moment he looked down into the flames which were rising to where he stood; and as he looked the indescribable horror which flitted over his features might have worked upon the devil himself to relent. His words were few.

'My child,' said he, 'is still safe; she is an infant, a young crathur that never harmed you nor any one—she is still safe. Your mothers, your wives, have young, innocent childhre like it. Oh, spare her! think for a moment that it's one of your own. Spare it, as you hope to meet a just God; or if you don't, in mercy shoot me first—put an end to me before I see her burned!'

The captain approached him coolly and deliberately. 'You'll prosecute no one now, you bloody informer,' said he; 'you'll convict no more boys for takin' an ould gun an' pistol from you, or for givin' you a neighbourly knock or two into the bargain.'

Just then, from a window opposite him, proceeded the shrieks of a woman, who appeared at it with the infant in her arms. She herself was almost scorched to death; but, with the presence of mind and humanity of her sex, she was about to put the little babe out of the window. The captain noticed this, and, with characteristic atrocity, thrust, with a sharp bayonet, the little innocent, along with the person who endeavoured to rescue it, into the red flames, where they both perished. This was the work of an instant. Again he approached the man. 'Your child is a coal now,' said he, with deliberate mockery; 'I pitched it in myself, on the point of this'—showing the weapon—'an' now is your turn'—saying which he clambered up, by the assistance of his gang, who stood with a front of pikes and bayonets bristling to receive the wretched man, should he attempt, in his despair, to throw himself from the wall. The captain got up, and placing the point of his bayonet against his shoulder, flung him into the fiery element that raged behind him. He uttered one wild and terrific cry as he fell back, and no more. After this nothing was heard but the crackling of the fire and the rushing of the blast: all that had possessed life within were consumed, amounting either to eleven or fifteen persons.

When this was accomplished, those who took an active part in the murder stood for some time about the conflagration; and as it threw its red light upon their fierce faces and rough persons, soiled as they now were with smoke and black streaks of ashes, the scene seemed to be changed to hell, the murderers to spirits of the damned, rejoicing over the arrival and the torture of some guilty soul. The faces of those who kept aloof from the slaughter were blanched to the whiteness of death; some of them fainted, and others were in such agitation that they were compelled to lean on their comrades. They became actually powerless with horror; yet to such a scene were they brought by the pernicious influence of Ribbonism.

It was only when the last victim went down that the conflagration shot up into the air with most unbounded fury. The house was large, deeply thatched, and well furnished; and the broad red pyramid rose up with fearful magnificence towards the sky. Abstractedly it had sublimity, but now it was associated with nothing in my mind but blood and terror. It was not, however, without a purpose that the captain and his gang stood to contemplate its effect. 'Boys,' said he, 'we had betther be sartin that all's safe; who knows but there might be some of the sarpents crouchin' under a hape o' rubbish, to come out an' gibbet us to-morrow or next day. We had betther wait awhile, anyhow, if it was only to see the blaze.'

Just then the flames rose majestically to a surprising height. Our eyes followed their direction; and we perceived, for the first time, that the dark clouds above, together with the intermediate air, appeared to reflect back, or rather to have caught, the red hue of the fire. The hills and country about us appeared with an alarming distinctness; but the most picturesque part of it was the effect or reflection of the blaze on the floods that spread over the surrounding plains. These, in fact, appeared to be one broad mass of liquid copper, for the motion of the breaking waters caught from the blaze of the high waving column, as reflected in them, a glaring light, which eddied, and rose, and fluctuated as if the flood itself had been a lake of molten fire.

Fire, however, destroys rapidly. In a short time the flames sank—became weak and flickering—by-and-by they shot out only in fits—the crackling of the timbers died away—the surrounding darkness deepened—and ere long the faint light was overpowered by the thick volumes of smoke that rose from the ruins of the house and its murdered inhabitants.

'Now, boys,' said the captain, 'all is safe—we may go. Remember, every man of you, what you've sworn this night on the book an' althar of God—not on a heretic Bible. If you perjure yourselves, you may hang us; but let me tell you, for your comfort, that if you do there is them livin' that will take care the lase of your own lives will be but short.'

After this we dispersed every man to his own home.

Reader, not many months elapsed ere I saw the bodies of this captain, whose name was Patrick Devann, and all those who were actively concerned in the perpetration of this deed of horror, withering in the wind, where they hung gibbeted near the scene of their nafarious villainy; and while I inwardly thanked heaven for my own narrow and almost undeserved escape, I thought in my heart how seldom, even in this world, justice fails to overtake the murderer, and to enforce the righteous judgment of God—that 'whoso sheddeth man's blood, by man shall his blood be shed.'

This tale of terror is, unfortunately, too true. The scene of hellish murder in it lies at Wildgoose Lodge, in the county of Louth, within about four miles of Carrickmacross, and nine of Dundalk. No such multitudinous murder has occurred, under similar circumstances, except the burning of the Sheas in the county of Tipperary. The name of the family burned in Wildgoose Lodge was Lynch. One of them had, shortly before this fatal night, prosecuted and convicted some of the neighbouring Ribbonmen, who visited him with severe marks of their displeasure in consequence of his having refused to enrol himself as a member of their body.

The language of the story is partly fictitious; but the facts are pretty closely such as were developed during the trial of the murderers. Both parties were Roman Catholics. There were, if the author mistake not, either twenty-five or twenty-eight of

those who took an active part in the burning hanged or gib-
betted in different parts of the county of Louth. Devann, the
ringleader, hung for some months in chains, within about a
hundred yards of his own house, and about half a mile from
Wildgoose Lodge. His mother could neither go into nor out of
her cabin without seeing his body swinging from the gibbet.
Her usual exclamation on looking at him was, 'God be good
to the sowl of my poor marthyr!' The peasantry, too, frequently
exclaimed on seeing him, 'Poor Paddy!'—a gloomy fact that
speaks volumes.

A WICKED SPELL

When a girl wishes to gain the love of a man, and to make him marry her, a dreadful spell called 'Drimial Agus Thorial' is used. At dead of night, she and an accomplice go to a church-yard, exhume a newly-buried corpse, and take a strip of the skin from the head to the heel. This is wound round the girl as a belt with a solemn invocation to the devil for his help.

After she has worn it for a day and a night she watches her opportunity and ties it round the sleeping man whose love she desires; during which process the name of God must not be mentioned.

When he awakes the man is bound by the spell; and is forced to marry the cruel and evil harpy. It is said the children of such marriages bear a black mark round the wrist and are known and shunned by the people, who call them; 'sons of the devil'.

THE ISLAND MAGEE TERROR
JIM MCGARRY

Island Magee, is not despite its name, really an island, joined
as it is to the coast of Co. Antrim. In 1710, James Hattridge,
son of the late Presbyterian Minister in Island Magee, was
living there with his young wife and family in a solid,
comfortable home, which they shared with his widowed
mother. September of that year saw the beginning of the
terrible events that were to befall the family, events that
were later to affect a very large part of the county of Antrim,
and become forever associated with Ireland's history of witchcraft and legend. Between September 1710, and her death
the following February, this harmless old widow Hattridge
was to become the unfortunate object of manifestations, the
continuance of which reduced the family to a state of abject
terror.

Widow Hattridge's torment began as she sat at the family
fireside one evening, and was without warning bombarded
by a hail of stones. They struck her back and shoulders but
did not injure her. This, however, was only the beginning
of the old lady's ordeal, and at night she was disturbed in
bed by pillows being pulled from under her head and blankets
stripped from over her. Very frightened, she persuaded the
young girl of the household to sleep in her room, but it
made no difference. Her bed continued to be stripped except
when a candle was lit in order to search the room, when
the phenomena ceased.

Old, feeble, and frightened widow Hattridge then betook
herself to the room of her son and daughter-in-law and
there enjoyed some peace for a number of weeks. December
came, and one evening, as she was sitting by the fireside in
the twilight, she found herself joined by a small boy in ragged
clothes. Her kindly offer of food and clothing went unan-
swered. His face remained covered with rags though she

127

asked to see it. Finally he ran from the fireside, departing as suddenly as he had come.

This boy was to become in the months that followed the uninvited and unwanted guest of the Hattridge household. He broke windows with stones, threw furniture round the house and stole a book of sermons much treasured by the old lady. Familiarity with this strange boy did not bring peace, and he soon became involved in a more sinister incident. He was found by a maid servant in the garden digging what seemed to be a grave with a sword. He told the girl that it was for a member of the family who would soon die, thus adding further elements to a situation already beyond the comprehension of the simple people upon whom he had intruded.

Early February 1711 saw the family tense and very disturbed by all that was happening to them. The room vacated by the old widow seeking the comfort and reassurance of her son and his wife, was by now disarranged as often as the family could put it in order. The bedclothes kept forming into the shape of a corpse with the covering undermost, blankets and bolster above them and the sheets spread overall. Eight days of this reduced everybody in the household to a state of near collapse.

The help of the local Minister, the Rev. Mr Sinclair, was finally sought. He, with two of his elders, decided to stay all day and all night with the family in the house, praying for their safe deliverance. Persuaded by them to sleep again in her room, Widow Hattridge was unable to get any rest and at about midnight she cried out suddenly and moaned. Answering the minister's question, she declared that she was in very great pain, with something like a knife being pressed into her back. Their prayer and help being unavailing, she was removed the following morning to another room where she spent the last week of her life continually tormented by the same severe pain in her back. Eventually, on the 22nd February, she finally died; happily her end was relatively peaceful.

Following her burial, peace and quiet came to the house and her son travelled on business to Dublin, in those days a far distant place. His young wife and family, as well as the servants, were still in a very disturbed state, so Mrs Hattridge persuaded her sister and a cousin, Mary Dunbar, to live with them for company until her husband returned. Mary Dunbar was young and beautiful, a stranger to the neighbourhood, who on the very first night of her arrival was to find herself involved in a train of events of the kind associated with the afflicted household. She soon became its most miserable victim.

The night of her arrival was marked before bedtime by clothes being taken from trunks all over the house and scattered in the most unlikely places. Some were thrown out of doors, and while efforts were being made to tidy up this strange confusion, an apron was found rolled and tied with its own string, in which there were five knots of a strange kind. Now terrified by they knew not what, the family refused to undo them, but young Mary Dunbar volunteered and proceeded to unravel each one and so perhaps unwittingly involved herself beyond recall.

The next day, Mary Dunbar, although young and healthy, was seized with the most violent pains in her thigh which caused her to fall down, crying out in agony. After a few minutes' respite, the pain returned to the same place, as well as her head, her back and her breast. They recurred every seven or eight minutes until late in the afternoon, when she fell into a fit, struggling and shouting wildly. At intervals she appeared to talk to some unseen persons.

On recovery she was asked by the family to whom she had been speaking during all this, and she replied that her conversation had been with an old woman, whom she described, and several others who, she claimed, were threatening to kill her. She was asked if she knew the people, and while she could describe them in some considerable detail, she said she had never seen them before in her life.

During these fits she had heard them name each other, one being called Janet Main and the other Janet Carson. She refused to go any further in her description or speak any more of it, saying that they had threatened dire consequences if she told too much. During continuing fits throughout the following night and day, she was again clearly heard speaking to people invisible to the rest of the family, as well as praying to God for her own safety.

Recovering from a succession of attacks a day or two later, she again named Janet Carson as one of her tormentors. On this occasion a daughter of Janet Carson was in the house and became very upset at the naming of her mother as a witch by Mary Dunbar. She immediately went to the Rev. Sinclair, whose advice to her was to prevail upon her mother to make a neighbourly visit to the sick Mary and discover whether she knew her or not. Janet Carson was reluctant to do this but under pressure from Rev. Sinclair and others, finally allowed herself to be persuaded.

Mary Dunbar was a complete stranger to the neighbourhood and had never been nearer than fifteen or twenty miles to the place, which, in those days of primitive travel, was a fair distance. Hence she had no knowledge of Janet Carson. Yet as the woman approached the house and before anyone could see her, Mary became very frightened and called out, 'There's Janet Carson.' While the woman remained in the room, Mary was in such a state of terror and agony that it took three strong men to hold her in her bed. Later that night, following Janet Carson's departure, clothes were taken off the bed and were found burning in the grate of the empty parlour and large stones were thrown at servants. However, neither the thrower nor any other stranger was seen.

Mary Dunbar, on the following day, still suffered from acute pains but, perhaps encouraged by her revelation of her first tormentor, she gave descriptions of two other women whom she alleged were persecuting her. She declared they were often in bed with her and would laugh, jeer and cause her great misery. She described one as being a woman of low build with a swarthy face, large rolling eyes and a lame foot. In the company of this creature was a younger, more comely woman of about the same height, who also was lame. Neighbours present, after consideration, decided that her description might well fit one Mrs Janet Sellor and her daughter Elizabeth.

These events inevitably led to Janet Sellor being asked if she would, with her daughter, visit Mary Dunbar, but she absolutely refused. She had announced that if the devil had taken the health from the girl, then the devil should give her health again—and to the devil with the lot of them. Sellor had been for a great many years regarded as a witch in the area and recently her daughter had gained a similar reputation. Her landlord William Fenton, learning of her attitude, with the help of other prominent people of the distict, eventually prevailed upon the woman to come with her daughter to see the girl.

Word of these happenings spread throughout the neighbourhood and quite a large number of people gathered at Mr Hattridge's house to await the visit. They were joined once more by the Rev. Sinclair, and also by his curate, Rev. David Robb. Being by now greatly concerned by the events which had taken place, Mr Sinclair decided that about thirty of the women gathered there should go one by one into the room where Mary Dunbar lay, to ascertain beyond doubt whether the girl was sure of her identifications. However, Mary Dunbar remained completely peaceful, declaring that none of those brought before her were her tormentors, until last of all Janet Sellor appeared. As soon as she arrived at the door Mary cried aloud that it was she. While Sellor remained in the room Mary was in a dreadfully agitated state and quite clearly in great pain. Once again she had to be restrained as she lay in torment in her bed. Janet Sellor prayed to God to send her back her health and the people present, in trembling and fear, cried out aloud on seeing the miserable condition of the wretched girl.

Disturbed and distressed by the events befalling his God-fearing and law-abiding congregation, Mr Sinclair, in an effort to relieve what was rapidly becoming an unbearable situation, took the daughter Elizabeth Sellor into the room. To his horror Mary Dunbar once more fell into a fit, and only on her removal did she become peaceful. Still unsatisfied, the ministers arranged a test whereby Mary turned her face to the wall so that she could not see anybody coming into the room. Several innocent women were brought in with no results, but when Elizabeth Sellor entered Mary reacted as violently as before, and was quietened only on her removal.

Night brought no quiet as the girl's fits continued inter-mittently, and a heavy sulphurous smell was noticed by those present. Mary's description of her torment through the night included pains in her body as though pricked with pins and a burning heat at her breast as though she were roast-ing. She called for water at each recovery and drank large quantities of it though she was unable to eat or drink any-thing else. Sometimes, with throat contracted and teeth set, she appeared in danger of choking and continually struggled with a violent pain in her hands and feet. Despairing of all else, her relations carried her from the room and on taking her across the threshold she went into a posture of death for some time, her body becoming completely rigid and much heavier than normal.

The change of room brought no relief to her condition, and on Sunday, 5th March, she proceeded to name another of her tormentors as Catherine. She described her as a large dark woman but failed to identify many women of that name who were brought to her from the area. Finally one Catherine M'Calmond was brought. M'Calmond had a repu-tation of irreligion and infamy and only with the greatest difficulty was she persuaded to visit the house. Her entry into the room threw Mary into a violent convulsion and on recovery she charged M'Calmond with being one of her tormentors. Some hours afterwards, recovering from a further series of fits, she told those present that during them she had seen Catherine M'Calmond, Janet Carson and two other women, whom she named as Janet Main and Lattimer.

On Monday 6th March in an atmosphere of growing tension, the Mayor of Carrickfergus issued a warrant for the arrests of Janet Carson, Catherine M'Calmond, Janet Sellor and Elizabeth Sellor. They were taken into custody at 10 am and brought to Carrickfergus, where they were com-mitted to jail while a prosecution was being arranged.

Later that evening, Mary again fell into her fits and was obviously suffering very great pain. When she recovered, she once more named the women Main and Lattimer, saying that they had come upon her in her bed and put their hands on her mouth, upon which her teeth were closed and her tongue pulled back. Janet Main, she said, was a woman of middle stature with very small brown eyes, a short nose and a mark upon her breast. Lattimer she described as a tall black woman, very ill-coloured. She declared that they had told her she should not listen to the Rev. Sinclair's prayers which signified nothing. Since they served a better master, she would soon be well if she would do as they told her.

Following these incidents, fear spread like wild-fire through the district, and searches were made for women answering the description given by her of Main and Lattimer. A woman named Janet Lattimer was found in the Irish quarter of Carrickfergus and a Janet Main in the parish of Broad Island. Both of these women answered in detail the descriptions given by Mary Dunbar, and they both had bad reputations in their neighbourhoods. Immediately a warrant was issued by the Justice of the Peace to apprehend them and bring them to the girl for a confrontation.

Lattimer, after much persuasion but of her own accord, was brought first, and on her arrival at the house was proved to be completely unknown to any of those present. No sooner, however, had she entered the door, than Mary Dunbar called out, 'There's Lattimer' and became delirious. Janet Main was brought later, unannounced, accompanied by several other women also unknown to Mary. None of these women in any way agitated her until Main entered, whereupon the girl became so demented that she lost all power of speech and fell into a violent fit before a large number of witnesses. Main's removal brought immediate peace and calm. Janet Main's husband being unsatisfied, it was decided to confront the girl once more with his wife, but on her entry Mary Dunbar again became violent and accused her of being one of her cruellest tormentors. She alleged Main and Lattimer had threatened to destroy her if she gave information on them as she had done with others before them.

Main and Lattimer were taken that afternoon by a constable before the Mayor of Carrickfergus and committed to jail, arrangements being made for their prosecution. Mary Dunbar then became peaceful and enjoyed an undisturbed sleep that night.

During the days following the arrest of these two women, Mary Dunbar enjoyed great peace and was able to go in and out of her room without trouble, and even to eat frequently. It was also noticed that the sulphurous smell no longer pervaded the house. However, on Sunday, March 11th, she was anxious to go to church where she joined in the Psalms and prayer. Before the conclusion of the service however, she became very ill and had to be taken outside. On recovery, she insisted on returning to the service, only to suffer yet more agony until she was finally brought home where her torment continued throughout the day. Those present heard her calling out in a scarcely audible voice, and when she was a little better she said that she had seen a red-haired woman blind in one eye, which was sunk in her red face.

A woman of a neighbouring parish who fitted this description was brought before her, but she remained completely undisturbed. During the day several others in the area were brought to her without any obvious effect.

That night was a most troublesome one for the household, as well as several neighbours who had volunteered to stay with the family and comfort them in their great distress. Doors opened of their own volition, noises were heard, and several people were actually struck by things thrown at them from they knew not where. During the night Mary took some long hairs from her mouth during several fits and in intervals of calmness continued to give the descriptions of those who tormented her. Her description of the woman with the sunken blind eye was particularly graphic, down to such details as the side of her face being drawn together by smallpox and her fingers crooked in at the ends.

At noon on the Monday, the Mayor, accompanied by some of his officials, came to question and examine Mary Dunbar. During the questioning she became delirious several times but in between times was able to answer their questions and to swear a statement. She stated that the six women then in custody—Janet Carson, Janet Sellor, Elizabeth Sellor, Janet Main, Catherine M'Calmond and Janet Lattimer—had been her tormentors but had left her alone since being taken into custody. On being asked by the Mayor as to whether there were any others who tormented her, she said that there were two, and gave clear descriptions of them. She further added that they, and her former tormentors, had told her that they would never cease until they put the whole family out of the house.

By now greatly distraught by these events, Mary's relations decided on Tuesday, March 13th that it would be better to take her from the Hattridge home and bring her to the home of a Mr Stannus in Larne, a journey requiring travel by horseback and then by boat. While on horseback she suffered some fits again and could not be prevented from falling to the ground several times, so violent did she become. In the boat she was ill almost continually and had further attacks after landing.

Recovering, she astonished those present by telling them that Janet Main and the woman with the blind eye had been with her throughout the journey and even after her arrival.

She was then warned to be careful of what she said, since it was public knowledge that Janet Main was in jail and therefore would not be able to give her any trouble. Despite this caution, she persisted in her statement. The following morning she continued to suffer, insisting that Janet Main was in bed with her. Because of her persistence, some of her relatives took the precaution of checking on whether or not Janet Main was still in jail. As a result of these enquiries, they learned from the Mayor of Carrickfergus that both Janet Main and Janet Sellor had been taken out of jail in the morning to the jailer's house, had their bolts struck off, and had been put to work spinning and carding wool. They were brought back to jail again and bolted in that night.

Meanwhile a large area around Larne was in the grip of both fear and curiosity, the result of a search of the greatest intensity for the woman blind in one eye. Several women with that affliction were brought to Mary, but none of them caused her any disturbance whatsoever. She was, in fact, very apologetic for the trouble caused to them in being brought to her. Eventually a woman was discovered in Carrickfergus who, when challenged became enraged, cursing and swearing and protesting. With the greatest difficulty she was persuaded to come to Mary Dunbar, and while she was still within a quarter of a mile of the house, Mary began to sweat and tremble, and act as though acutely afraid. On her entering the house, Mary was subjected to a fit more horrifying than any observed before; she had to be forcibly restrained in her bed by several people. When the woman was removed to a barn, Mary immediately became easier and was then asked if she was certain beyond doubt thàt this was the woman she described as her torturer. She said that she was and that she knew her well; she certainly fitted the descriptions Mary had given earlier.

This woman, Janet Miller, was then questioned in great detail by the Rev. Ogilvy of Larne, without being able to give any satisfactory answers. He asked her what she thought was the reason for the girl becoming so ill on her approach and why Mary Dunbar could so accurately describe her without having seen or heard of her previously. She answered in a most surly manner, 'I believe the devil's in the lass.' Still doubting, some of those present decided upon another trial and took Miller to the house without Mary Dunbar's knowledge. The effect was exactly the same as on the previous occasion. She was immediately sent to Carrickfergus and there jailed. On searching her house, the authorities found a ball of hair made of the roots of herbs with a needle five inches long through it which they threw in the fire and burned. It was noted after this that one of Mary's most dreadful symptoms, that of her tongue becoming drawn back and lodged in her throat causing her to choke, ceased and did not recur.

The following day Mary again suffered from many attacks and later told those present that a woman she had mentioned earlier, called Mrs Ann, had appeared to her and accused her of having the others discovered and imprisoned. She threatened not to leave until she had caused Mary's death. Mary having given a complete description, a search was immediately set up. After a day of comparative ease on the Friday, her attacks resumed on Saturday and she told those present that Mrs Ann was with her and threatening to destroy her. She complained of a pain in her arm as if it were being amputated, and when it was examined they found a black woollen string with eight knots tied in it wrapped around her arm. It was immediately cut off and her pain ended. She later complained of a pain in her thigh and this too was found to have a knotted cord on it, the removal of which brought relief at once. Later in the afternoon of the same day, a blue string with five knots was found on her arm. She then complained that her back and waist were in great pain and the Rev. Skevington of Larne found a white string tied round her waist with nine knots upon it. During the night she complained of severe pain in her right arm, and a white woollen string with five knots was discovered round it. In all cases the removal of the string terminated the suffering immediately. By now Mary's friends and relatives were in a state of near distraction, terrified of what each day and night might bring. Sunday proved their worst fears to be well founded. Mary went into convulsions very early in the morning and after the first one was heard to proclaim that Mrs Ann had been putting hair, feathers and pins down her throat, and had threatened to use knives next, and destroy her the following day. Very shortly afterwards she suffered from the most violent pains in the stomach for a protracted period and then vomited some very coarse horse hair. Through the day and into the night she continued to vomit, disgorging five large pins with a quantity of woollen feathers. She remained extremely ill throughout the night, with attack following attack in rapid succession.

Since she had given a fairly detailed picture of Mrs Ann, a widespread search was mounted, as a result of which Margaret Mitchell, of the parish of Kilroot, was found to bear the marks described by Mary when examined by some of the observers who had heard the descriptions. Following some protest on her part, she was brought to Mary's house and her approach sent the girl into a state of terror. When she was taken into the room, Mary, although in obvious fear, openly accused her of being one of her greatest tormentors. The Rev. Ogilvy then warned Mary to be most careful of accusing anybody of such a crime, but the girl replied vehemently that, as she would answer before God at the Day of Judgement, Mitchell was the person who went under the name of Mrs Ann. Being by now reluctant to add to the number in jail,

137

Mary's relatives allowed Mitchell to go free, but Mary continued to have further attacks and always, when she recovered, accused Mitchell. During the following days, she vomited quantities of feathers, two buttons, and four large pins, two of them very badly rusted.

While these events were taking place in Larne, the Hattridge home had found neither peace nor quiet on Mary's departure. The contents of the house were continually found in complete disarray, inexplicable noises disturbed the family and their neighbours by day and night, and most noticeably, string, cords, and even children's clothes were found with strange knots in them.

Mary's relations were disturbed by the continuance of her sufferings after Mitchell was freed and they decided to bring the accused woman to the girl for the second time. At the woman's approach, Mary once more suffered a severe fit and, when Mitchell was removed, persisted in her accusations that this was Mrs Ann and the person she described. During the evening of the same day at about seven o'clock, Mary vomited a long linen thread with seven knots on it, which appeared in her mouth and was pulled from her throat by some of those present. Convinced by now that Mitchell had a hand in the girl's sufferings, the woman was arrested by John Logan, Constable of Broad Island, and put in bolts at Ballycarry at about eleven o'clock that evening. Following her incarceration, Mary improved considerably in health.

Legal investigations were now actively proceeding, and in an effort to ensure that justice would be done, it was decided to carry out an experiment. Janet Main and Janet Sellor were released for a time and their bolts struck off to see if, as had occurred on a previous occasion, Mary would suffer any disturbance. Simultaneously with their release, she was seized with fits and seemed to be terrified of something. Recovering, she said that Janet Main and Janet Sellor had appeared to her and had threatened her. She also vomited large quantities of feathers and six very large pins. Later that day when Main and Sellor had been re-arrested, she was seen to relax into peace and contentment.

The law took its course, and arrangements were made for

the trials at Carrickfergus. On the day before they were due to commence, Mary Dunbar set out about two o'clock in the afternoon on her journey to give evidence against those she had accused. During her journey she had more fits, making it necessary to lodge her overnight in the home of one John Burns. She told those present that in her seizures on the road a man with light, greying-brown hair and very shabby clothes had appeared to her. He had threatened her for helping the prosecution of women at the assizes. He warned her that she would not have the power to speak in court and told her they would torment her more terribly than they had done at any time before. Shortly afterwards she did lose the use of her tongue and continued to lose it at intervals throughout the night and on the following day during her journey.

Through the hours before the trial, which was set for the strange hour of six o'clock in the evening, Mary had further attacks, accompanied by loss of speech. When the trial began she took her place in court but suffered several fainting fits. Although obviously hearing very well except during these attacks, she was completely unable to speak. Evidence was given before the Court by four clergymen, Mr and Mrs James Hattridge and many prominent citizens who had been witnesses of the events which had occurred. They were able to swear to the extraordinary features of Mary's time of terror and tribulation.

Following a long trial, the verdict of the jury was that Janet Sellor, Elizabeth Sellor, Janet Carson, Catherine M'Calmond, Janet Main, Janet Lattimer, Janet Miller and Margaret Mitchell were guilty of exercising witchcraft on the body of Mary Dunbar. They were sentenced to be imprisoned for twelve months and to be pilloried four times.

The trial over, Mary was taken on horseback to the home of her mother in Castlerech, County Down, but her own trial had not yet ended. She continued to suffer pain, terror and distress, with regular recurrence of her fits until, after a very bad incident, she described William Sellor, the husband of Janet Sellor. He had fled in fear of being arrested, but was captured only four miles away and taken to the girl. She declared that he had appeared to her with a butcher's knife, the blade of which was broken, and threatened to kill her. She claimed that it wounded her under her right shoulder, and on examination her shoulder was found to have a clearly visible mark upon it. The High Constable, on this evidence, arrested Sellor and his trial took place at the following assizes, where he was found guilty. After the first trial the Hattridge home had continued to be disturbed by mysterious noises and other phenomena, but following Sellor's trial neither the Hattridge home nor Mary suffered further.

Since Mary Dunbar's frightful afflictions, the case has remained very much alive in the annals of Irish witchcraft. Many of its features differ somewhat from witchcraft cases recorded elsewhere, as for instance the extraordinary ability of Mary Dunbar to describe in great detail her tormentors, thus enabling her friends and the law to apprehend them. The comparatively light sentences imposed and the thoroughness of the legal investigation at Carrickfergus reflect an approach which was most unusual in a period when denunciation so often led to instant trial and burning. This, by the way, was the last witchcraft trial to be held in Ireland.

THE LEGEND OF NEAL-MOR

There is a great hole or well near the river Suir, always
filled with water, whose depth no man has yet fathomed.
Near it is a castle, which in old times belonged to a powerful
chief called Neal-Mor. One day, while his servants were stack-
ing the hay, a violent tempest of wind and rain came on, which
quite destroyed the crop. Then Neal-Mor was filled with
rage, and he mounted his horse and drew his sword, and rode
forth to the field; and there he challenged the Lord God
Himself to battle. And he swung his sword round his head
and struck at the air, as if he would kill and slay the
Great Invisible Spirit. On which suddenly a strange thing
happened, for a great whirlwind arose and the earth opened,
and Neal-Mor, still astride on his horse and with his sword
in his hand, was lifted high up into the air and then cast down
alive into the great hole, called Poul-mor, which may be
seen to this day, and the castle is still standing by the margin.
But no trace of Neal-Mor or his steed was ever again beheld.
They perished utterly by the vengeance of God.

But some time after his disappearance, a rude stone figure
seated on a horse was cast up out of the earth; and then
all men knew the fate of the terrible chief who had braved the
wrath of God, for here was his image and the sign of his
destruction. The stone figure is still preserved at the castle, and
tradition says that if it were removed, the whole castle would
crumble to pieces in a single night and be cast into the Poul-
mor.

MELMOTH
CHARLES MATURIN

Alive again? Then show me where he is;
I'll give a thousand pounds to look upon him.
SHAKESPEARE

In the autumn of 1816, John Melmoth, a student in Trinity College, Dublin, quitted it to attend a dying uncle on whom his hopes for independence chiefly rested. John was the orphan son of a younger brother, whose small property scarce could pay John's college expenses; but the uncle was rich, unmarried, and old; and John, from his infancy, had been brought up to look on him with that mingled sensation of awe, and of the wish, without the means to conciliate, (that sensation at once attractive and repulsive), with which we regard a being who (as nurse, domestic, and parent have tutored us to believe) holds the very threads of our existence in his hands, and may prolong or snap them when he pleases.

On receiving this summons, John set immediately out to attend his uncle.

The beauty of the country through which he travelled (it was the county Wicklow) could not prevent his mind from dwelling on many painful thoughts, some borrowed from the past, and more from the future. His uncle's caprice and moroseness,—the strange reports concerning the cause of the secluded life he had led for many years,—his own dependent state,—fell like blows fast and heavy on his mind. He roused himself to repel them,—sat up in the mail, in which he was a solitary passenger,—looked out on the prospect,—consulted his watch;—then he thought they receded for a moment,—but there was nothing to fill their place, and he was forced to invite them back for company. When the mind is thus active in calling over invaders, no wonder the conquest is soon completed. As the carriage drew near the Lodge, (the name of old Melmoth's seat), John's heart grew heavier every moment.

The recollection of this awful uncle from infancy,—when he was never permitted to approach him without innumerable lectures,—*not to be troublesome*,—not to go too near his uncle,—not to ask him any questions,—on no account to disturb the inviolable arrangement of his snuff-box, hand-bell, and spectacles, nor to suffer the glittering of the gold-headed cane to tempt him to the mortal sin of handling it,—and, finally, to pilot himself aright through his perilous course in and out of the apartment without striking against the piles of books, globes, old newspapers, wig-blocks, tobacco-pipes, and snuff-canisters, not to mention certain hidden rocks of rat-traps and mouldy books beneath the chairs,—together with the final reverential bow at the door, which was to be closed with cautious gentleness, and the stairs to be descended as if he were 'shod with felt.'—This recollection was carried on to his school-boy years, when at Christmas and Easter, the ragged pony, the jest of the school, was dispatched to bring the reluctant visitor to the Lodge,—where his pastime was to sit vis-à-vis to his uncle, without speaking or moving, till the pair resembled Don Raymond and the ghost of Beatrice in the Monk,—then watching him as he picked the bones of lean mutton out of his mess of weak broth, the latter of which he handed to his nephew with the needless caution not to 'take more than he liked,'—then hurried to bed by daylight, even in winter, to save the expense of an inch of candle, where he lay awake and restless from hunger, till his uncle's retiring at eight o'clock gave signal to the governante of the meagre household to steal up to him with some fragments of her own scanty meal, administering between every mouthful a whispered caution not to tell his uncle. Then his college life, passed in an attic in the second square, uncheered by an invitation to the country; the gloomy summer wasted in walking up and down the deserted streets, as his uncle would not defray the expenses of his journey;—the only intimation of his existence, received in quarterly epistles, containing, with the scanty but punctual remittance, complaints of the expenses of his education, cautions against extravagance, and lamentations for

143

the failure of tenants and the fall of the value of lands. All these recollections came over him, and along with them the remembrance of that last scene, where his dependence on his uncle was impressed on him by the dying lips of his father.

'John, I must leave you, my poor boy; it has pleased God to take your father from you before he could do for you what would have made this hour less painful to him. You must look up, John, to your uncle for every thing. He has oddities and infirmities, but you must learn to bear with them, and with many other things too, as you will learn too soon. And now, my poor boy, may He who is the father of the fatherless look on your desolate state, and give you favour in the eyes of your uncle.' As this scene rose to John's memory, his eyes filled fast with tears, which he hastened to wipe away as the carriage stopped to let him out at his uncle's gate.

He alighted, and with a change of linen in a handkerchief, (his only travelling equipment), he approached his uncle's gate. The lodge was in ruins, and a barefooted boy from an adjacent cabin ran to lift on its single hinge what had once been a gate, but was now a few planks so villainously put together, that they clattered like a sign in a high wind. The stubborn post of the gate, yielding at last to the united strength of John and his barefooted assistant, grated heavily through the mud and gravel stones, in which it left a deep and sloughy furrow, and the entrance lay open. John, after searching his pocket in vain for a trifle to reward his assistant, pursued his way, while the lad, on his return, cleared the road at a hop step and jump, plunging through the mud with all the dabbling and amphibious delight of a duck, and scarce less proud of his agility than of his 'sarving a gentleman.' As John slowly trod the miry road which had once been the approach, he could discover, by the dim light of an autumnal evening, signs of increasing desolation since he had last visited the spot,—signs that penury had been aggravated and sharpened into downright misery. There was not a fence or a hedge round the domain: an uncemented wall of loose stones, whose numerous gaps were filled with furze or thorns, supplied their place. There was not a tree or shrub on the lawn; the lawn itself was turned into pasture-ground, and a few sheep were picking their scanty food amid the pebble-stones, thistles, and hard mould, through which a few blades of grass made their rare and squalid appearance.

The house itself stood strongly defined even amid the darkness of the evening sky; for there were neither wings, or offices, or shrubbery, or tree, to shade or support it and soften its strong harsh outline. John, after a melancholy gaze at the grass-grown steps and boarded windows, 'addressed himself' to knock at the door; but knocker there was none: loose stones, however, there were in plenty; and John was making vigorous application to the door with one of them, till the furious barking of a mastiff, who threatened at every bound to break his chain, and whose yell and growl, accompanied by 'eyes that glow and fangs that grin,' savoured as much of hunger as of rage, made the assailant raise the siege on the door, and betake himself to a well-known passage that led to the kitchen. A light glimmered in the window as he approached: he raised the latch with a doubtful hand; but, when he saw the party within, he advanced with the step of a man no longer doubtful of his welcome.

Round a turf-fire, whose well-replenished fuel gave testimony to the 'master's' indisposition, who would probably as soon have been placed on the fire himself as seen the whole *kish* emptied on it once, were seated the old housekeeper, two or three *followers*, (*i.e.* people who ate, drank, and lounged about in any kitchen that was open in the neighbourhood, on an occasion of grief or joy, all for his 'honour's' sake, and for the great 'rispict' they bore the family), and an old woman, whom John immediately recognized as the doctress of the neighbourhood,—a withered Sybil, who prolonged her squalid existence by practising on the fears, the ignorance, and the sufferings of beings as miserable as herself. Among the better sort, to whom she sometimes had access by the influence of servants, she tried the effects of some simples, her skill in which was sometimes productive of success. Among the lower orders she talked much of the effects of the 'evil eye,' against which she boasted a counter-spell of unfailing efficacy; and while she spoke, she shook her grizzled locks with such witch-like eagerness, that she never failed to communicate to her

half-terrified, half-believing audience, some portion of that
enthusiasm which, amid all her consciousness of imposture,
she herself probably felt a large share of; still, when the case
at last became desperate, when credulity itself lost all patience,
and hope and life were departing together, she urged the miserable patient to confess *there was something about his heart;*
and when this confession was extorted from the weariness of
pain and the ignorance of poverty, she nodded and muttered
so mysteriously, as to convey to the bystanders, that she had
had difficulties to contend with which were invincible by
human power. When there was no pretext, from indisposition,
for her visiting either 'his honour's' kitchen, or the cottar's
hut,—when the stubborn and persevering convalescence of the
whole country threatened her with starvation,—she still had a
resource:—if there were no lives to be shortened, there were
fortunes to be told;—she worked 'by spells, and by such
daubry as is beyond our element.' No one twined so well as she
the mystic yarn to be dropped into the lime-kiln pit, on the
edge of which stood the shivering inquirer into futurity, doubtful whether the answer to her question of 'who holds?' was
to be uttered by the voice of demon or lover.

No one knew so well as she to find where the four streams
met, in which, on the same portentous season, the chemise
was to be immersed, and then displayed before the fire, (in the
name of one whom we dare not mention to 'ears polite'), to
be turned by the figure of the destined husband before morning. No one but herself (she said) knew the hand in which
the comb was to be held, while the other was employed in
conveying the apple to the mouth,—while, during the joint
operation, the shadow of the phantom-spouse was to pass across
the mirror before which it was performed. No one was more
skilful or active in removing every iron implement from the
kitchen where these ceremonies were usually performed by
the credulous and terrified dupes of her wizardry, lest, instead
of the form of a comely youth exhibiting a ring on his white
finger, a headless figure should stalk to the rack (*Anglicè*,
dresser), take down a long spit, or, in default of that, snatch
a poker from the fire-side, and mercilessly take measure with
its iron length of the sleeper for a coffin. No one, in short,

146

knew better how to torment or terrify her victims into a belief
of that power which may and has reduced the strongest minds
to the level of the weakest; and under the influence of which the
cultivated sceptic, Lord Lyttleton, yelled and gnashed and
writhed in his last hours, like the poor girl who, in the
belief of the horrible visitation of the vampire, shrieked aloud,
that her grandfather was sucking her vital blood while she
slept, and expired under the influence of imaginary horror.
Such was the being to whom old Melmoth had committed his
life half from credulity, and (*Hibernicè* speaking) *more than
half* from avarice. Among this group John advanced,—recog-
nising some,—disliking more,—distressing all. The old housekeeper received him with cordiality;—he was always her 'white-
headed boy,' she said,—(*imprimis*, his hair was as black as jet),
and she tried to lift her withered hand to his head with an
action between a benediction and a caress, till the difficulty
of the attempt forced on her the conviction that that head was
fourteen inches higher than her reach since she had last patted
it. The men, with the national deference of the Irish to a
person of superior rank, all rose at his approach, (their stools
chattering on the broken flags), and wished his honour 'a
thousand years, and long life to the back of that; and would
not his honour take something to keep the grief out of his
heart;' and so saying, five or six red and bony hands tendered
him glasses of whiskey all at once. All this time the Sybil
sat silent in the ample chimney-corner, sending redoubled
whiffs out of her pipe. John gently declined the offer of spirits,
received the attentions of the old housekeeper cordially, looked
askance at the withered crone who occupied the chimney-
corner, and then glanced at the table, which displayed other
cheer than he had been accustomed to see in his 'honour's
time.' There was a wooden dish of potatoes, which old Melmoth
would have considered enough for a week's subsistence. There
was the salted salmon, (a luxury unknown even in London.
Vide Miss Edgeworth's Tales, 'The Absentee').

There was the *slink-veal*, flanked with tripe; and finally,
there were lobsters and *fried* turbot enough to justify what the
author of the tale asserts, 'suo periculo,' that when his great
grandfather, the Dean of Killala, hired servants at the deanery,

they stipulated that they should not be required to eat turbot or lobster more than twice a week. There were also bottles of Wicklow ale, long and surreptitiously borrowed from his 'honour's' cellar, and which now made their first appearance on the kitchen hearth, and manifested their impatience of further constraint, by hissing, spitting, and bouncing in the face of the fire that provoked its animosity. But the whiskey (genuine illegitimate potsheen, smelling strongly of weed and smoke, and breathing defiance to excisemen) appeared, the 'veritable Amphitryon' of the feast; every one praised, and drank as deeply as he praised.

John, as he looked round the circle, and thought of his dying uncle, was forcibly reminded of the scene at Don Quixote's departure, where, in spite of the grief caused by the dissolution of the worthy knight, we are informed that 'nevertheless the niece eat her victuals, the housekeeper drank to the repose of his soul, and even Sancho cherished his little carcase.' After returning, 'as he might,' the courtesies of the party, John asked how his uncle was. 'As bad as he can be;' —'Much better, and many thanks to your honour,' was uttered in such rapid and discordant unison by the party, that John turned from one to the other, not knowing which or what to believe. 'They say his honour has had a fright,' said a fellow, upwards of six feet high, approaching by way of whispering, and then bellowing the sound six inches above John's head. 'But then his honour has had *a cool* since,' said a man who was quietly swallowing the spirits that John had refused. At these words the Sybil who sat in the chimney corner slowly drew her pipe from her mouth, and turned towards the party: The oracular movements of a Pythoness on her tripod never excited more awe, or impressed for the moment a deeper silence. 'It's not *here*,' said she, pressing her withered finger on her wrinkled forehead, 'nor *here*,—nor *here*;' and she extended her hand to the foreheads of those who were near her, who all bowed as if they were receiving a benediction, but had immediate recourse to the spirits afterwards, as if to ensure its effects.—'It's all *here*—it's all *about the heart*;' and as she spoke she spread and pressed her fingers on her hollow bosom with a force of action that thrilled her hearers.—'It's all *here*,' she

148

added, repeating the action, (probably excited by the effect she had produced), and then sunk on her seat, resumed her pipe, and spoke no more. At this moment of involuntary awe on the part of John, and of terrified silence on that of the rest, an unusual sound was heard in the house, and the whole company started as if a musket had been discharged among them:—it was the unwonted sound of old Melmoth's bell. His domestics were so few, and so constantly near him, that the sound of his bell startled them as much as if he had been ringing the knell for his own internment. 'He used always to *rap down* for me,' said the old housekeeper, hurrying out of the kitchen; 'he said pulling the bells wore out the ropes.'

The sound of the bell produced its full effect. The house-keeper rushed into the room, followed by a number of women, (the Irish præficæ), all ready to prescribe for the dying or weep for the dead,—all clapping their hard hands, or wiping their dry eyes. These hags all surrounded the bed; and to witness their loud, wild, and desperate grief, their cries of 'Oh! he's going, his honour's going, his honour's going,' one would have imagined their lives were bound up in his, like those of the wives in the story of Sinbad the Sailor, who were to be interred alive with their deceased husbands.

Four of them wrung their hands and howled round the bed, while one, with all the adroitness of a Mrs Quickly, felt his honour's feet, and 'upward and upward,' and 'all was cold as any stone.'

Old Melmoth withdrew his feet from the grasp of the hag,—counted with his keen eye (keen amid the approaching dimness of death) the number assembled round his bed,—raised himself on his sharp elbow, and pushing away the housekeeper, (who attempted to settle his nightcap, that had been shoved on one side in the struggle, and gave his haggard, dying face, a kind of grotesque fierceness), bellowed out in tones that made the company start,—'What the devil brought ye all here?' The question scattered the whole party for a moment; but rallying instantly, they communed among themselves in whispers, and frequently using the sign of the cross, muttered 'The devil, —Christ save us, the devil in his mouth the first word he spoke.' 'Aye,' roared the invalid, 'and the devil in my eye the first
149

sight a see.' 'Where,—where?' cried the terrified housekeeper, clinging close to the invalid in her terror, and half-hiding herself in the blanket, which she snatched without mercy from his struggling and exposed limbs. 'There, there,' he repeated, (during the battle of the blanket), pointing to the huddled and terrified women, who stood aghast at hearing themselves arointed as the very demons they came to banish. 'Oh! Lord keep your honour's head,' said the housekeeper in a more soothing tone, when her fright was over; 'and sure your honour knows them all, is'n't *her* name,—and *her* name,—and *her* name,'—and she pointed respectively to each of them, adding their names, which we shall spare the English reader the torture of reciting, (as a proof of our lenity, adding the last only Cotchleen O'Mulligan). 'Ye lie, ye b——h,' growled old Melmoth; 'their name is Legion, for they are many,—turn them all out of the room,—turn them all out of doors,—if they howl at my death, they shall howl in earnest,—not for my death, for they would see me dead and damned too with dry eyes, but for want of the whiskey that they would have stolen if they could have got at it,' (and here old Melmoth grasped a key which lay under his pillow, and shook it in vain triumph at the old housekeeper, who had long possessed the means of getting at the spirits unknown to his 'honour'), 'and for want of the victuals you have pampered them with.' '*Pampered*, oh Ch—st!' ejaculated the housekeeper. 'Aye, and what are there so many candles for, all *fours*, and the same below I warrant. Ah! you—you—worthless, wasteful old devil.' 'Indeed, your honour, they are all *sixes*.' 'Sixes,—and what the devil are you burning sixes for, d'ye think it's *the wake* already? Ha?' 'Oh! not yet, your honour, not yet,' chorussed the beldams; 'but in God's good time, your honour knows,' in a tone that spoke ill-suppressed impatience for the event. 'Oh! that your honour would think of making your soul.' 'That's the first sensible word you have said,' said the dying man, 'fetch me the prayer-book,—you'll find it there under that old boot-jack,—blow off the cobwebs;—it has not been opened this many a year.' It was handed to him by the old governante, on whom he turned a reproaching eye. 'What made you burn sixes in the kitchen, you extravagant jade? How many years have you lived in this house?' 'I don't know, your honour.' 'Did you ever see any extravagance or waste in it?' 'Oh never, never, your honour.' 'Was any thing but a farthing candle ever burned in the kitchen?' 'Never, never, your honour.' 'Were not you kept as tight as hand and head and heart could keep you, were you not? answer me that.' 'Oh yes, sure, your honour; every *sowl* about us knows that,—every one does your honour justice, that you kept the closest house and closest hand in the country,—your honour was alway a good warrant for it.' 'And how dare you unlock my hold before death has unlocked it,' said the dying miser, shaking his meagre hand at her. 'I smelt meat in the house,—I heard voices in the house,—I heard the key turn in the door over and over. Oh that I was up,' he added, rolling in impatient agony in his bed, 'Oh, that I was up, to see the waste and ruin that is going on. But it would kill me,' he continued, sinking back on the bolster, for he never allowed himself a pillow; 'it would kill me,—the very thought of it is killing me now.' The women, discomfited and defeated, after sundry winks and whispers, were huddling out of the room, till recalled by the sharp eager tones of old Melmoth.— 'Where are ye trooping to now? back to the kitchen to gormandize and guzzle? Won't one of ye stay and listen while there's a prayer read for me? Ye may want it one day for yourselves, ye hags.' Awed by this expostulation and menace, the train silently returned, and placed themselves round the bed, while the housekeeper, though a Catholic, asked if his honour would not have a clergyman to give him *the rights,* (rites) of his church. The eyes of the dying man sparkled with vexation at the proposal. 'What for,—just to have him expect a scarf and hat-band at the funeral. Read the prayers yourself, you old——; that will save something.' The housekeeper made the attempt, but soon declined it, alleging, as her reason, that her eyes had been watery ever since his honour took ill. 'That's because you had always a drop in them,' said the invalid, with a spiteful sneer, which the contraction of approaching death stiffened into a hideous grin.—'Here,—is not there one of you that's gnashing and howling there, that can get up a prayer to keep me from it?' So adjured, one of the women offered her services; and of her it might truly be said, as of the 'most desartless man of the watch' in Dogberry's time, that 'her reading and writing came by nature;' for she never had been at school, and had never before seen or opened a Protestant prayer book in her life; nevertheless, on she went, and with more emphasis than good discretion, read nearly through the service for the 'churching of women;' which in our prayer-books following that of the burial of the dead, she perhaps imagined was someway connected with the state of the invalid.

She read with great solemnity,—it was a pity that two interruptions occurred during the performance, one from old Melmoth, who, shortly after the commencement of the prayers, turned towards the old housekeeper, and said, in a tone scandalously audible, 'Go down and draw the niggers of the kitchen fire closer, and lock the door, and let me *hear it locked*. I can't mind any thing till that's done.' The other was from John Melmoth gliding into the room, hearing the inappropriate words uttered by the ignorant woman, taking quietly as he knelt beside her the prayer-book from her hands, and reading in a suppressed voice part of that solemn service which, by the forms of the Church of England, is intended for the consolation of the departing.

'That is John's voice,' said the dying man; and the little kindness he had ever shewed this unfortunate lad rushed on his hard heart at this moment, and touched it. He saw himself, too, surrounded by heartless and rapacious menials; and slight as must have been his dependence on a relative whom he had always treated as a stranger, he felt at this hour he was no stranger, and grasped at his support like a straw amid his wreck. 'John, my good boy, you are there.—I kept you far from me when living, and now you are nearest me when dying.—John, *read on*.' John, affected deeply by the situation in which he beheld this *poor man*, amid all his wealth, as well as by the solemn request to impart consolation to his dying moments, read on;—but in a short time his voice became indistinct, from the horror with which he listened to the increasing hiccup of the patient, which, however, he struggled with from time to time, to ask the housekeeper if *the niggers were closed*. John, who was a lad of feeling, rose from his knees in some degree of agitation. 'What, are you leaving me like the rest?' said old Melmoth, trying to raise himself in the bed. 'No, Sir,' said John, 'but,' observing the altered looks of the dying man, 'I think you want some refreshment, some support, Sir.' 'Aye, I do, I do, but whom can I trust to get it for me? *They*, (and his haggard eye wandered round the group), *they* would poison me.' 'Trust me, Sir,' said John; 'I will go to the apothecary's, or whoever you may employ.' The old man grasped his hand, drew him close to his bed, cast a threatening yet fearful eye round the party, and then whispered in a voice of agonized constraint, 'I want a glass of wine, it would keep me alive for some hours, but there is not one I can trust to get it for me,—*they'd steal a bottle, and ruin me*.' John was greatly shocked. 'Sir, for God's sake, let *me* get a glass of wine for you.' 'Do you know where?' said the old man, with an expression in his face John could not understand. 'No, Sir; you know I have been rather a stranger here, Sir.' 'Take this key,' said old Melmoth, after a violent spasm; 'take this key, there is wine in that closet,—*Madeira*. I always told them there was nothing there, but they did not believe me, or I should not have been robbed as I have been. At one time I said it was whiskey, and then I fared worse than ever, for they drank twice as much of it.'

John took the key from his uncle's hand; the dying man pressed it as he did so, and John, interpreting this as a mark of kindness, returned the pressure. He was undeceived by the whisper that followed,—'John, my lad, don't drink any of that wine while you are there.' 'Good God!' said John, indignantly throwing the key on the bed; then, recollecting that the miserable being before him was no object of resentment, he gave the promise required, and entered the closet, which no foot but that of old Melmoth had entered for nearly sixty years. He had some difficulty in finding out the wine, and indeed stayed long enough to justify his uncle's suspicions,—but his mind was agitated, and his hand unsteady. He could not but remark his uncle's extraordinary look, that had the ghastliness of fear superadded to that of death, as he gave him permission to enter his closet. He could not but see the looks of horror which the women exchanged as he approached it. And, finally, when he was in it, his memory was malicious enough to suggest some faint traces of a story, too horrible for imagination, connected with it. He remembered in one moment most distinctly, that no one but his uncle had ever been known to enter it for many years.

Before he quitted it, he held up the dim light, and looked around him with a mixture of terror and curiosity. There was a great deal of decayed and useless lumber, such as might be supposed to be heaped up to rot in a miser's closet; but John's eyes were in a moment, and as if by magic, riveted on a portrait that hung on the wall, and appeared, even to his untaught eye, far superior to the tribe of family pictures that are left to moulder on the walls of a family mansion. It represented a man of middle age. There was nothing remarkable in the costume, or in the countenance, but *the eyes*, John felt, were such as one feels they wish they had never seen, and feels they can never forget. Had he been acquainted with the poetry of Southey, he might have often exclaimed in his after-life,

> 'Only the eyes had life,
> They gleamed with demon light.'—THALABA.

From an impulse equally resistless and painful, he approached the portrait, held the candle towards it, and could distinguish the words on the border of the painting,—Jno. Melmoth, anno 1646. John was neither timid by nature, nor nervous by constitution, or superstitious from habit, yet he continued to gaze in stupid horror on this singular picture, till, aroused by his uncle's cough, he hurried into his room. The old man swallowed the wine. He appeared a little revived; it was long since he had tasted such a cordial,—his heart appeared to expand to a momentary confidence. 'John, what did you see in that room?' 'Nothing, Sir.' 'That's a lie; every one wants to cheat or to rob me.' 'Sir, I don't want to do either.' 'Well, what did you see that you—you took notice of?' 'Only a picture, Sir.' 'A picture, Sir!—the original is still alive.' John, though under the impression of his recent feelings, could not but look incredulous. 'John,' whispered his uncle;—'John, they

say I am dying of this and that; and one says it is for want of
nourishment, and one says it is for want of medicine,—but
John,' and his face looked hideously ghastly, 'I am dying of
a fright. That man,' and he extended his meagre arm towards
the closet, as if he was pointing to a living being; 'that man, I
have good reason to know, is alive still.' 'How is that possible,
Sir?' said John involuntarily, 'the date on the picture is 1646.'
'You have seen it,—you have noticed it,' said his uncle. 'Well,'—
he rocked and nodded on his bolster for a moment, then,
grasping John's hand with an unutterable look, he exclaimed,
'You will see him again, he is alive.' Then, sinking back on
his bolster, he fell into a kind of sleep or stupor, his eyes still
open, and fixed on John.

The house was now perfectly silent, and John had time
and space for reflection. More thoughts came crowding on
him than he wished to welcome, but they would not be re-
pulsed. He thought of his uncle's habits and character, turned
the matter over and over again in his mind, and he said to himself, 'The last man on earth to be superstitious. He never
thought of any thing but the price of stocks, and the rate of
exchange, and my college expenses, that hung heavier at his
heart than all; and such a man to die of a fright,—a ridiculous
fright, that a man living 150 years ago, is alive still, and yet—
he is dying.' John paused, for facts will confute the most
stubborn logician. 'With all his hardness of mind, and of
heart, he is dying of a fright. I heard it in the kitchen, I
have heard it from himself,—he could not be deceived. If I
had ever heard he was nervous, or fanciful, or superstitious,
but a character so contrary to all these impressions;—a man
that, as poor Butler says, in his Remains of the Antiquarian,
would have "sold Christ over again for the numerical piece of
silver which Judas got for him,"—such a man to die of fear!
Yet he *is* dying,' said John, glancing his fearful eye on the
contracted nostril, the glazed eye, the drooping jaw, the whole
horrible apparatus of the *facies Hippocratica* displayed, and
soon to cease its display.

Old Melmoth at this moment seemed to be in a deep
stupor; his eyes lost that little expression they had before,
and his hands, that had convulsively been catching at the

blankets, let go their short and quivering grasp, and lay extended on the bed like the claws of some bird that had died of hunger,—so meagre, so yellow, so spread. John, unaccustomed to the sight of death, believed this to be only a sign that he was going to sleep; and, urged by an impulse for which he did not attempt to account to himself, caught up the miserable light, and once more ventured into the forbidden room,—the *blue chamber* of the dwelling. The motion roused the dying man;—he sat bolt upright in his bed. This John could not see, for he was now in the closet; but he heard the groan, or rather the choked and guggling rattle of the throat, that announces the horrible conflict between muscular and mental convulsion. He started, turned away; but, as he turned away, he thought he saw the eyes of the portrait, on which his own was fixed, *move*, and hurried back to his uncle's bedside.

Old Melmoth died in the course of that night, and died as he had lived, in a kind of avaricious delirium. John could not have imagined a scene so horrible as his last hours presented. He cursed and blasphemed about three half-pence, missing, as he said, some weeks before, in an account of change with his groom, about hay to a starved horse that he kept. Then he grasped John's hand, and asked him to give him the sacrament. 'If I send to the clergyman, he will charge me something for it, which I cannot pay,—I cannot. They say I am rich,—look at this blanket;—but I would not mind that, if I could save my soul.' And, raving, he added, 'Indeed, Doctor, I am a very poor man. I never troubled a clergyman before, and all I want is, that you will grant me two trifling requests, very little matters in your way,—save my soul, and (whispering) make interest to get me a parish coffin,—I have not enough left to bury me. I always told every one I was poor, but the more I told them so, the less they believed me.'

John, greatly shocked, retired from the bed-side, and sat down in a distant corner of the room. The women were again in the room, which was very dark. Melmoth was silent from exhaustion, and there was a death-like pause for some time. At this moment John saw the door open, and a figure appear at it, who looked round the room, and then quietly and deliberately retired, but not before John had discovered in his face the living original of the portrait. His first impulse was to utter an exclamation of terror, but his breath felt stopped. He was then rising to pursue the figure, but a moment's reflection checked him. What could be more absurd, than to be alarmed or amazed at a resemblance between a living man and the portrait of a dead one! The likeness was doubtless strong enough to strike him even in that darkened room, but it was doubtless only a likeness; and though it might be imposing enough to terrify an old man of gloomy, and retired habits, and with a broken constitution, John resolved it should not produce the same effect on him.

But while he was applauding himself for this resolution, the door opened, and the figure appeared at it, beckoning and nodding to him, with a familiarity somewhat terrifying. John now started up, determined to pursue it; but the pursuit was stopped by the weak but shrill cries of his uncle, who was struggling at once with the agonies of death and his house-keeper. The poor woman, anxious for her master's reputation and her own, was trying to put on him a clean shirt and nightcap, and Melmoth, who had just sensation enough to perceive they were taking something from him, continued exclaiming feebly, 'They are robbing me,—robbing me in my last moments.—robbing a dying man. John, won't you assist me,—I shall die a beggar; they are taking my last shirt,—I shall die a beggar.'—And the miser died.

THE DEAD

The great and old families of Ireland consider it right to be buried with their kindred, and are brought from any distance, however remote, to be laid in the ancient graveyard of the race.

A young man of family having died far away, from fever, it was thought advisable not to bring him home, but to bury him where he died. However, on the night of the funeral a phantom hearse with four black horses stopped at the churchyard. Some men then entered with spades and shovels and dug a grave, after which the hearse drove away. But next morning no sign of the grave was to be found, except a long line marked out, the length of a man's coffin.

It is unlucky and a bad omen to carry fire out of a house where any one is ill. A gentleman one day stopped at a cabin to get a light for his cigar, and having wished good morning in the usual friendly fashion, he took a stick from the fire and blew it into a blaze. He was walking away, when the woman of the house rose up fiercely and told him it was an evil thing to take fire away when her husband was dying. On looking round he saw a wretched skeleton lying on a bed of straw, so he flung back the stick at once, and fled from the place, leaving his blessing in the form of a silver offering, to neutralize the evil of the abducted fire.

Fontana Tales of Terror

Stories to chill your blood from every corner of the globe.
Along with tidbits of haunting history and strange happenings
never yet explained—for the truth is often even more hair-
raising than the imaginary.

Tales of Terror from Outer Space
Welsh Tales of Terror
Edited by R. Chetwynd-Hayes

London Tales of Terror
Edited by Jacquelyn Visick

Scottish Tales of Terror
Edited by Angus Campbell

European Tales of Terror
Sea Tales of Terror
Edited by J. J. Strating

Fontana also publishes

The Invisible Man
H. G. Wells

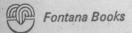
Fontana Books

Fontana Books

Fontana is best known as one of the leading paperback publishers of popular fiction and non-fiction. It also includes an outstanding, and expanding, section of books on history, natural history, religion and social sciences.

Most of the fiction authors need no introduction. They include Agatha Christie, Hammond Innes, Alistair MacLean, Catherine Gaskin, Victoria Holt and Lucy Walker. Desmond Bagley and Maureen Peters are among the relative newcomers.

The non-fiction list features a superb collection of animal books by such favourites as Gerald Durrell and Joy Adamson.

All Fontana books are available at your bookshop or newsagent; or can be ordered direct. Just fill in the form below and list the titles you want.

FONTANA BOOKS, Cash Sales Department, G.P.O. Box 29, Douglas, Isle of Man, British Isles. Please send purchase price, plus 8p per book. Customers outside the U.K. send purchase price, plus 10p per book. Cheque, postal or money order. No currency.

NAME (Block letters)

ADDRESS